PRAISE FOR FLOW IN THE KIT(

HEALTHY STRESS-FREE \

"I will never say "I hate cooking!" again. I thought I needed a meal delivery service when really I needed this book. Finding *Flow in the Kitchen* has been a surprise, a relief and a delight."

—Oonagh Duncan, fitness expert
Author of *Healthy as F*ck [Ditch the Diet]*
fitfeelsgood.com

"Have you lost your passion for the kitchen? Want to make healthy and delicious meals that are ethical and environmentally friendly, but you can't muster the time or energy? *Flow in the Kitchen* can help. This intelligent, sensitive and informative book will reinvigorate your love of cooking real foods. Bringing mindful meal planning into your home will make the time you spend in the kitchen a joy."

—Pamela Fergusson, Ph.D., Registered Dietitian
Author of *Going Vegan for Beginners*
pamelafergusson.com

"*Flow in the Kitchen* makes cooking as easy as sweeping! Even the most advanced cooks will find tips for cooking mindfully and efficiently."

—Élise Desaulniers, author of Cash Cow:
Ten Myths About the Dairy Industry
Co-author of *Tables véganes*, winner of a Taste Canada Gold Award
edesaulniers.com

"Brigitte has created the perfect guide to support your transition to a healthy, kind and compassionate way of eating and living. The book shows you how a vegan diet does not have to be complicated or burdensome, but rather it is nutritious, healthy, tasty, fun and achievable. I highly recommend this book as your companion to a healthy plant-based way of living."

—Dr. Shireen Kassam, Founder of Plant-Based Health Professionals UK

Author of *Eating Plant-Based: Scientific Answers to Your Nutrition Questions*
shireenkassam.medium.com

"Cooking can be stressful, but it doesn't have to be. *Flow In the Kitchen* shares an enlightened approach to plant-based food preparation that will benefit anyone that wants to eat healthier. Let Brigitte guide you to cook more easily – and joyfully!"

—Dreena Burton

Author of *Dreena's Kind Kitchen* and *Plant-Powered Families*
dreenaburton.com

This book will be a must-have for anyone looking to make the jump to plant-based cooking. It's a comprehensive look at not only what to cook, but the "how" behind, it without giving up your life.

—Amanda Spackman, registered dietitian

Host of the Planned, Prepped, and Productive Podcast
callmebetty.com

"*Flow in the Kitchen* has completely changed my attitude, and therefore my results, in the kitchen! I used to be a lousy cook and resented having to do it. Yet this book helped me not only understand why I hated cooking, but also helped me change my mindset about it. I actually enjoy cooking now. I love nourishing myself and my family and prefer my own food to restaurant food! And although I initially scoffed at the idea that I may not need recipes or that I might know more than I think about plant-based cooking, she's right! With her guidance, I'm learning to "take off the training wheels" and become more experimental. I don't need to rely on recipes quite as much as I used to. I continue to gain confidence and joy in the kitchen and I cannot recommend this book enough!"

—Marian Erikson, host of the Plant Based Briefing Podcast
plantbasedbriefing.com

"To say that *Flow in the Kitchen* is not a cookbook is an understatement: it is a well thought out book that delivers much more than cooking. It's a not a light read, rather "meaty" (or veggie), that requires thought. It delivers on the goal of getting you to step into the kitchen and add joy to your vegan food. Even though the author and I disagree on cooking grains in the Instant Pot, this book is true vegan food for thought. I highly recommend taking the time to read this vegan and life manifesto to get to the heart of understanding flow in the kitchen, and beyond."

—Jill Nussinow, The Veggie Queen, nutritionist, and culinary educator
Author of *Vegan Under Pressure* and other cookbooks
theveggiequeen.com

"Brigitte has solved the problem of sustainable cooking habits by laying out a system to change your narrative and relationship with preparing healthy food with interest, joy, and calm."

—Maša and Michael Ofei, creators of Heartful Table

Authors of *The Minimalist Vegan*

heartfultable.com

Flow in the Kitchen

Practices for Healthy Stress-Free Vegan Cooking

BRIGITTE GEMME

Published by Low Impact Lab

Copyright © 2022 by Brigitte Gemme

Title: Flow in the kitchen: practices for healthy stress-free vegan cooking

Names: Gemme, Brigitte, author

Paperback ISBN: 978-1-7387018-1-0

Author photo credit: Jānis Hofmanis

Book design by Jonas Perez Studio

Cover design by Nadya Matatova

low impact lab

ABOUT THE AUTHOR

Brigitte Gemme is passionate about helping more people eat more plants, empowering others to take charge of their health and live in alignment with their values. On her website *VeganFamilyKitchen.com*, she teaches regular workshops about all aspects of healthy vegan cooking, from mindset to meal planning, from nutrition boosters to batch cooking. Hundreds of home cooks are free from having to decide what's for dinner thanks to Brigitte's Vegan Meal Plan service. She previously worked in academic research management in the fields of education, sociology, and clean energy. After undergraduate studies in Science, Technology, and Society, Brigitte completed a Ph.D. in Educational Studies at the University of British Columbia and a certificate in Plant-Based Nutrition from the University of Winchester. She lives in Vancouver (Canada) with her husband and two children.

To my mother. Thank you for cooking.

Contents

Preface Cookbooks don't cook   13

PART ONE PRACTICING FLOW IN THE KITCHEN   17

    Chapter 1 To flow, start with an anchor   23

    Chapter 2 Conscious compromise   37

    Chapter 3 Why we resist cooking   43

    Chapter 4 To find flow, find joy   51

    Chapter 5 The making of a healthy vegan meal   61

    Chapter 6 Weekly meal planning as visualization   71

    Chapter 7 Batch cooking to save lives   87

    Chapter 8 Start with the minimum viable prep   95

    Chapter 9 Cooking mindfully   105

    Chapter 10 Keep the really good food flowing   117

PART TWO UNDERSTANDING HEALTHY VEGAN COOKING   127

    Cooking whole grains   129

    Cooking dry beans from scratch   135

    Soups and stews   147

    Stir-fries   159

Salads and bowls   167

Pizza   175

Instant sauces   183

Vegetables to buy every week   191

Must-have pantry ingredients   199

Keep on learning   **209**

Acknowledgments   **211**

Download your Flow in the Kitchen Kit   **213**

Preface

Cookbooks don't cook

The purpose of this book is to inspire you to cook more vegan, plant-based meals at home using (mostly) whole foods. I will guide you through the practices that will induce a state of flow in your kitchen. When you start – and continue – practicing, you will enjoy the process of cooking *really good food* for yourself and your loved ones. Cooking will come with more ease and less stress.

To enjoy flow, a collection of 100 recipes accompanied by drool-inducing photographs of food in ceramic bowls laid out on wooden boards, with a sprinkle of decorative peppercorns and a fork at just the right angle, is the last thing you need.

Cookbooks with artfully styled photographs are selling more copies than ever. I admit to owning a few dozen myself. My collection makes a great decoration in the kitchen. I love leafing through them to learn new tricks from some of the best vegan recipe developers. I fantasize about dinner parties I would host featuring some of those creations. Every year, there are new, gorgeous ones published that I add to my Christmas list.

Sadly, the commercial success of cookbooks does not translate into more delicious and nutritious meals cooked at home from wholesome plant ingredients. Worldwide, food delivery services like Uber Food and DoorDash are booming. How many of us frequently eat out or buy ready-made meals, despite our piles of cookbooks, fridges full of fresh produce, and cabinets crammed with cookware?

Some of those options are better than others, but in general ready-made dishes from restaurants and frozen aisles have too much salt, refined sugar, and saturated fat. They also have less of what our bodies and souls need to thrive, like vegetables, whole grains, and legumes. Above all, ready-made dishes lack love. They are not cooked *for you* by someone who *loves you*.

If you struggle with the daily challenge of coming up with healthy dinners that are efficient to prepare and enjoyable to eat, adding another cookbook to your shelf won't be the game-changer you need. It's time to try something else.

With *Flow in the Kitchen*, I invite you to explore a different path. This book introduces you to a comprehensive method to think about and actually cook the *really good food* that best suits your needs and those of your loved ones.

Like other meaningful journeys, the road to practicing flow in the kitchen requires a commitment of time and energy. Some discomfort may be involved. With practice, you will experience the bliss of focused, confident, and joyful cooking with growing frequency.

My role is to inspire, motivate, and guide you to embark on this journey, stick with it as you encounter obstacles, and get back on track when your practice gets disrupted. Your role is to decide whether you will start – and continue – practicing flow in the kitchen.

Does preparing meals stress you out? Do you resent having to cook every day? Do you sometimes say, "I hate cooking"? I invite you to embark on this different kind of journey.

Do you feel that the food you end up eating does not nourish you? Does it fail to reflect your values and aspirations? Does it feel like your meals hurt rather than heal? Let's see if another way of thinking about cooking can help.

Would you like to move with ease and joy in the kitchen? Join me in the practice of flow in the kitchen.

We are made from what we eat. Our food determines how we show up in the world for ourselves and others. Imagine a life in which you feel nourished and energized, physically and mentally, thanks to the really good food you cook. Visualize yourself stepping into the kitchen with your whole heart and mind, embracing the task with joy, efficiently cooking really good food... and then moving on to other important pursuits in your life.

Engaging with the practices in this book and adapting them to suit your circumstances will change your life.

PART ONE

PRACTICING FLOW IN THE KITCHEN

Flow in a healthy vegan kitchen means the practice of preparing nourishing meals in a focused, confident, and joyful way. Practicing flow means letting go of distractions, frustrations, and worries. Your flow practice will bring answers to the questions that plague you as a home cook: What am I going to cook? How am I going to go about it? Are my loved ones going to eat it? Will the food I serve help us thrive? What am I missing out on while I am stuck in the kitchen cooking?

Flow is not only about cooking but rather about the complete process of planning, preparing, and serving meals. Cooking is *one* of those steps, and not even the most important. Feeling at ease and comfortable – not struggling – in the kitchen depends on the quality of our presence as we plan, prepare, and serve our meals.

Flow practices take time and effort, but they need not take over our entire lives. However, they do deserve our full attention for a few hours every week.

Reaching a state of flow on a day-to-day basis requires thoughtfully adjusting cooking plans to fit available resources, including knowledge, skill, time, money, equipment, and ingredients. Every day, there will be conscious compromises, reflecting our effort to do the best we can with what we have.

Flow in a healthy vegan kitchen is a virtuous circle. The more we practice it, the more our skills will develop, the more our sense of flow will expand.

And practice, you must.

Cooking isn't different from other kinds of exercises of the body and mind. Whether you are improving your fitness, developing a creative skill like painting, or learning to live more mindfully, you don't expect to be able to succeed at everything you try for the first time. One would not show up for the first day of karate class and expect to chop a board with their bare hand.

Cooking is the same. To get better at it, daily practice is essential.

Unfortunately, many of us practice cooking in a way that hinders flow. I do it myself on occasion. Here is what it looks like:

Dinner time is approaching. We browse our cookbooks or search the Internet, then choose a recipe for which we have most of the ingredients. Or we watch witty short videos on social media demonstrating how to cook something that looks amazing, then perhaps try to repeat the procedure in our own kitchen… or mindlessly swipe to the next one. At some point, we settle on a dish to cook and scramble to pull it together, frequently referring to the instructions on our phone for guidance. Often, we make a mess. Later in the evening, as we wash more dishes than we'd like, our mind drifts to tomorrow: what should we cook for dinner next?

What is too often missing is intention and direction.

It's not necessary to be a master chef to enjoy a state of flow in the kitchen. In fact, with some conscious effort, beginners can achieve flow very early in their cooking practice — *if* they adjust their practice to the resources they have at hand.

Compare cooking to another kind of physical and mental endeavor: running. A new runner wouldn't try to run a marathon a month after their first 5K fun run (3 miles). Not necessarily because it would be impossible to run the whole distance (26.1 miles!), but because it would be a recipe for injury and disappointment — anything but flow. The runner might very well cross the marathon finish line... eventually. But it will be a long time before they wish to or are even able to run again. They would be better off trying an 8K or 10K race, or — better yet — attempting another 5K to see if they can run a little faster or enjoy it more. By beginning slowly and intentionally, they can enjoy the scenery and even experience "runner's high" as they gently stretch their fitness and stamina to run progressively longer distances. This ensures that they will want to run again another day.

Similarly, why would new plant-based cooks attempt complex recipes from cookbooks when just starting their cooking journey? And why would they try to achieve that feat on a Wednesday night when everyone is "hangry" and tired? Instead, I would advise they create a simple bean and vegetable stew with rice, and I bet they will enjoy both the process and the results more.

In this book, I invite you to reconsider your cooking – or to consider it for the first time – so you can reach and progressively expand your experience of flow in the kitchen with daily practice.

The phases of flow in the kitchen

The act of cooking is only one phase of the flow process that we need to practice to put really good food on the table day after day. The other phases – planning, preparing, serving, and reflecting upon meals – are often merely glossed over in cookbooks, briefly discussed in a few introductory pages that most readers skip over to get to the recipes and photos. Because the pre- and post-cooking phases are critical to practicing flow, they will get the most attention in this book.

Connecting with our "why" sets the stage to practice flow. In the first chapter, I will briefly review what motivates me to put so much effort into healthy vegan food for myself and my loved ones. I cannot think of anything more important than that, and I hope you will agree that the practice is worth your time as well. Chapter 2 – the most important of them all – will introduce you to the idea of conscious compromises. Flow is all about balancing priorities, including your values, health, and commitments.

In chapter 3, I will take you for a deep dive into the reasons why so many of us resist cooking. Once you see the big picture, you will want to zoom in to try some of the mindset tweaks I suggest to improve your cooking experience and practice. Even people who think they hate cooking can unlock a state of flow in the kitchen. Chapter 4 proposes many practical strategies to summon joy and fuel a state of flow.

Having understood the context in which we cook and improved our mindset about it, it will be time to talk about the healthy vegan food itself. Chapter 5 offers a method to compose balanced meals that are satisfying and nourishing. Chapter 6 introduces you to planning an entire week's worth of meals (or even two weeks). Weeknights will be less stressful once you learn how to pre-load much of the cooking work by creating and implementing your batch cooking plan, the topic of chapter 7. Chapter 8 offers detailed instructions for a "minimum viable prep" that will enable beginners and busy people to enjoy really good food all week long.

What if you could be fully present to the act of cooking? In chapter 9, I invite you to try mindful, screen-free cooking – a guaranteed way to cook faster and learn more as you do it.

Closing the loop, chapter 10 maps the review process I recommend to constantly improve our kitchen flow practice, increase ease, gently expand our comfort zone over time, and adjust to life's ebbs and flows.

What about recipes?

I don't think you need them. I am making the wager that you already know more than you think about healthy vegan cooking. Even if you are a complete beginner, you are aware that vegetables, whole grains, and beans must be involved. A healthy vegan meal can be as simple as that!

Still, I know you will look for something like a recipe, so I decided to offer a useful substitute: generic instructions for the most common healthy vegan dishes that you will want to cook every week. Some might call them "anti-recipes" or "recipe templates." In Part Two of this book, in addition to basic methods to cook whole grains and beans from scratch, I discuss soups and stews, stir-fries, salads and bowls, pizza, and basic sauces.

As you read those sections, you will absorb the instructions, creating mental pathways that you can later follow using almost any combination of healthy vegan ingredients. Improvising delicious and nutritious meals featuring seasonal produce and pantry ingredients will become your superpower! This will also give you a lens through which you can approach and understand recipes from other vegan bloggers and cookbook authors in the future, making it easier to substitute ingredients and adapt them to your needs.

I also provide lists of vegetables and pantry ingredients that you should always stock so that you can plan or improvise a broad variety of healthy plant-based dishes made with (mostly) whole foods.

In addition to the content of the book, I encourage you to download the set of free templates I created to help you plan, prepare, and reflect upon your weekly meals. See the last page of this book for the link.

As you adopt the habits described in this book and adapt them to your life, you will discover that practicing flow in the kitchen can be as nourishing as the food itself. Let's do it together.

CHAPTER 1

To flow, start with an anchor

There's a reason why prepared meals and processed foods are popular: they're convenient. They take away the need to think in depth about what we want to eat and how to make those meals happen, saving us from dealing with the messy process of cooking and cleaning up. In the last decade, ordering ready-made meals has allowed everyone to "just eat" and "skip the dishes."[1] Who can resist that?

This business sector is redefining "normal food" for most humans on Earth, quickly erasing memories of home cooking. Although everything and anything can be ordered, it's safe to say that the share of healthy and vegan meals among those billions of orders is insignificant.

In that context, my suggestion that one can find satisfaction and experience flow in planning, preparing, eating, and even cleaning up after healthy vegan meals seems quixotic. Am I profoundly disconnected from today's reality? Some may even accuse me of being ignorant of or insensitive to the plight of the toiling majority that simply has no time or energy to spare for cooking. Is it food shaming to point out that those fatty, salty, and sweet meals aren't benefiting anyone other than the corporations selling them?

Yet, I persist. I believe that there is no task more important in my life than preparing home-cooked healthy vegan meals for myself and my loved ones. If you are reading this book, you probably also have the intuition that a less-travelled path may also be, in the long run, a better choice for you and yours. What you do is ultimately up to you, but if you choose to attempt embracing a healthy vegan way of eating, I am here to empower you to find your own way.

To keep us motivated and committed as we attempt to stick with a practice that decidedly departs from the mainstream, we need to be clear about our "why." Finding what anchors our practice of flow in the kitchen – and revisiting it regularly – is necessary. Knowing why we channel our time and energy toward the planning, preparation, and enjoyment of healthy vegan food will keep us going day after day, week after week.

In this chapter, I share the stories that underpin my own motivations for embarking and staying on this path to cooking really good food for myself and my loved ones. I am not trying to convince anyone. Those are just the conclusions I have come to based on my own research, experience, and values. You will need to find out what facts and stories talk to you to break your own trail.

But first, what is really good food?

Your views may differ, but here are the characteristics that make food *really good* to me:

Really good food promotes good health. It's made from ingredients that are rich in fiber (the one nutrient that over 90% of North Americans are deficient in) and phytonutrients. It does not have excess added sodium, and its sugars and fats come from whole plant ingredients, like fruit and nuts. Daily meals are made from a variety of plant ingredients, keeping our microbiome happy and bringing in the full range of essential amino acids, vitamins, and minerals we need.

Really good food is kind to the planet. There are 8 billion people on Earth. We must share our small blue dot and responsibly use its resources so they will continue regenerating themselves and a biodiverse, beautiful life can thrive. That means reducing the amount of land we use for agriculture, not harvesting sea life from the ocean unless our survival depends on it, and drastically cutting back on pollution and greenhouse gas emissions. Eliminating animal products from our diet contributes to those goals.

Really good food avoids unnecessary suffering. We are lucky to live in an era when eating animals (including fish and insects) and animal secretions (milk and eggs) isn't needed for humans to thrive. Even those living in temperate climates can easily access everything they need for a balanced vegan diet.[2] We have access to a diversity of vegetables, grains, legumes,spices,

---

2 Those living close to the poles, in remote and rough areas, and on islands with a limited land base may not be so lucky... but that's a tiny proportion of our planet's population, and not a good reason for those who live in urban areas to eschew change.

nuts, and seeds that, together, are nutritionally superior to animal "foods." In addition, there simply isn't a way to feed 8 billion people any significant amount of meat, dairy, or eggs without resorting to cruel factory farming methods that cause suffering to animals and humans both. Why would we continue to consume animal products when we know that they come from hell?

Really good food comes from love. The energy and emotion that go into preparing our food at every step along the way become embedded in what we eat. From the rays of the sun that triggered a seed to sprout, to the sweat of the farm hand who picked the vegetable, to the mood of the cook who brought it all together, it all goes into the meal and then into the making of our bodies. What we eat – and how it was prepared – determines how we live our lives and show up into the world.

Really good food tastes good. Life is too short to endure foul-tasting food! Let's make dinner delicious. This said, our tastebuds can evolve and there is room for experimentation. I will try any combination of plant foods at least a few times before giving up on it.

Really good food is something to aspire to. Despite my best efforts, few meals I make embody all dimensions of *really good food*. But I keep trying because it's worth it.

Here's what drives my commitment.

I came for the environment

My grandfather was a dairy farmer, and my father eventually took over his herd of cows for a few years before turning to raising pigs. Working with animals was hard and dangerous.

Thankfully, by the time I turned 4, my parents sold the farm and opened a plant nursery.

We still lived in a mostly rural area, just on the edge of suburbia. Driving everywhere was the norm, and I was known as "nerdy" rather than "sporty" amongst my peers. Still, there was no outdoor activity I enjoyed more than riding my bicycle on the back roads of our little town. I loved the independence and freedom that came with rolling on my own two wheels! But my first love was books and, as a teenager, I figured out how to get on the bus and visit the libraries and book shops of the Big City: Montreal.

Eager to gain their freedom, most of my friends got their driver's license as soon as they turned 16. For reasons I didn't quite grasp at the time, I delayed getting mine. Instead, I moved to an apartment in the city's core and walked, biked, and took transit everywhere.

Urban cycling in the 1990s was great preparation for going vegan. Every day, 4,000-pound cars were trying to push me off narrow roads. In comparison, being asked where I get my calcium and protein sounds rather friendly. Under constant attack as a bike commuter, I embraced my two-wheeled community. Ready for confrontation, we had a long list of reasons why cycling is preferable to driving. Chief among those is the far lighter environmental footprint of velos compared to cars.

It is true that some bike commuters – like some vegans – can feel righteous, perhaps even smug, about their mode of transportation. I certainly did, until one day I read this comment on an online cycling bulletin board:

"If you ride your bike to work but eat beef to fuel yourself, you might as well be driving a Hummer."

The year was 2013. Almost 10 years later, I am grateful for that Internet stranger who virtually punched me in the gut.

Before then, I had never given a single thought to the environmental impact of my food choices. Raised on fresh, just-picked tomatoes, asparagus, and corn, I bemoaned the stale and hard imported vegetables found at the supermarket. Certainly, trucking them from far away must increase their carbon footprint. But eating animals was natural, necessary, normal, and nice – right? Rare steak and roasted chicken were my favorite things to eat, with cave-aged gruyere cheese a close third. Shining a light on the environmental wake of my dietary habits shattered my house of glass.

As I always do when faced with a challenge, I dove into books. Conveniently, the hard-nosed energy scholar Vaclav Smil (not a vegan) had just published *Should We Eat Meat?* His conclusion, though nuanced by 200 pages of history and calculations, was that meat production was woefully inefficient from an energy standpoint, and Western consumption of it excessive.

Some years prior, I had worked in the field of clean energy research. As someone who worried about catastrophic climate change, seeing the progress of technology up close disillusioned me. It seemed like there was no way so-called green energy could make a big-enough, fast-enough dent in our greenhouse gas emissions.

On the other hand, drastically cutting back on meat could rapidly slash emissions and pollution. Returning farmed land to wilderness would even allow many species to bounce back. Serious progress could be made in a decade or two if we got serious about it.

I liked to think of myself as a good citizen and felt the urge to do my share. By spring 2014, I had decided to make real efforts to eat more plants – and fewer animals – for the planet.

I stayed for the animals

For the next two years I lived as a flexible reducetarian: I taught myself how to cook vegan food at home, chose the vegetarian option at restaurants, and ate anything offered to me at relatives' or friends' homes.

I had a toddler and another child on the way, so learning about nutrition and what a well-planned vegan diet looked like was on top of my mind. Increasingly, I became confident that my family's nutritional needs could be met with a fully plant-based diet. Still, I enjoyed the taste of animal foods. Above all, I disliked making a scene and getting into conflict with loved ones.

Then, right around the time my second child was born, Élise Desaulniers, published a small but solid book called *Cash Cow* about the myths surrounding the dairy industry. Élise and I had many friends in common, so I felt inclined to trust her judgement. I was couch-bound, breastfeeding my newborn baby and cuddling him as he slept in my arms, so there was plenty of time to read. I blazed through *Cash Cow*'s nutritional, social, and political exposé in just a few hours.

I found myself amid another painful epiphany: cows make milk not because they are cows, but because they have babies – like me.

Duh.

Raised in a dairy family, I knew that cows were inseminated, experienced pregnancy for about the same time as human mothers. I was aware that they started lactating with the birth of their offspring. I also knew that baby cows ended up as veal. But, somehow, the social normalcy of dairy milk obscured the obvious, plain truth: cows were females exploited for their capacity to make milk after birthing babies.

As for eggs, I finally saw them for what they are: another product of a female's reproductive system. Eggs come from hens locked in small cages, popping out eggs at an unnatural and unsustainable pace that leads to organ prolapse and exhaustion.

Shame washed upon me one night as I cradled my newborn against my chest, caressing his bald head with the tips of my fingers. I imagined someone taking him out of my arms and auctioning him off to slaughter. The thought was so disturbing, it pains me to even write it.

Were the pleasure and convenience I enjoyed from consuming meat, dairy milk, eggs, and my beloved aged cheeses worth the unnecessary suffering they required? I could no longer think so. The next day, I woke up vegan not just at home, but in my whole life.

The health benefits keep me going

Health was not on my radar when I decided to start eating more plants and, eventually, go vegan. In fact, even after going vegan myself, I used to think that the health benefits of eating a plant-based diet were overblown by activists desperate to convince selfish consumers that eschewing animal products was a good idea.

Then, my father died.

Well, he didn't die right away. That's the issue with chronic disease. Yes, some people keel over instantly from a serious cardiac incident and cannot be reached by medical professionals fast enough to save their lives. However, the majority, like my father, go through a slow, tortuous process that stretches over months and often years. Doctor visits, drugs, fatigue, depression, pain, and medical procedures take over their lives. Meanwhile, loved ones also suffer from their protracted decline. Caregivers exhaust themselves at their side. Our health system crumbles under the weight of so many people who are so sick.

My father was the strongest and brightest man I knew, and extra sociable to boot. He always had fascinating and funny stories to tell. That was until he shrank into a shadow of himself. At first, he just behaved oddly, like the time he installed blinds onto my windows and left them slightly crooked. Dad had taught me that any job worth doing was worth doing well, so I was rather surprised when he waved off my concerns: "They're fine." Then, on a hot day, he stayed outside in the blazing sun for hours, ignoring my mothers' admonitions to come inside. Severely dehydrated, he left home in an ambulance and took 23 days to recover.

From the hospital, my mother called me to report that something *serious* was wrong with him: he had caused a scene by trying to fondle a nurse's body – something that was deeply out of character. What was wrong with him? Later, he became incontinent. My mother caught him putting away a used diaper in the closet for another day. Still in denial, she thought that my dad – ever one to tease others – was trying to be funny.

I regret having to share such embarrassing, sad details about my father's last years. But how else can I warn the world? Alzheimer's disease sneaks up on you or on someone you love, destroying so much of what makes life worth living. My father, a force of nature, could no longer walk more than a few steps or speak more than a few words. Eventually, he could no longer breathe.

To test his memory, doctors would often ask what he had for lunch. That was easy: my father had a ham sandwich on white bread every day of his life. Unsurprisingly, he also developed rectal cancer. For the rest of his life after surgery, he declined to eat high-fiber foods, wrongfully believing they would worsen his condition.

The connection between my father's diet and the dementia that slowly but fatally swallowed him is uncertain. He also had a regular, though seemingly not excessive, drinking habit, which didn't improve his odds. Overall, he just didn't put much credence in the idea of self-care or treating his earthly vessel with love. Like many of his siblings born in the post-Depression years, he believed in working hard until you no longer could, and that was that.

His decline and death put the issue of preventive health habits to the core of my consciousness. I am determined to avoid a similar fate for myself and my loved ones. Eating a vegan diet is a cornerstone of that commitment, along with living an active lifestyle, managing my stress, and connecting with my community.

Vegan food, however, is not healthy by default. I have a soft spot for donuts and peanut butter ice cream, and I am delighted that vegan versions of those treats are now available. However, those extra sweetened, fattened, and salted plant foods do not promote health any more than their non-vegan counterparts do.

A growing number of studies measuring diet with a tool called the *Healthy Plant-based Diet Index* report that unhealthy plant-based diets – consisting mostly of refined grains and foods with lots of added fat, sugar, and salt – carry similar health risks as non-plant-based diets when it comes to cardiovascular disease, type 2 diabetes, and dementia.

It may not be so much about the unhealthy foods we eat as it is about the healthy food we *don't* eat. Every meal is an opportunity to bring in nutrients that keep our arteries clean, our organs functioning, and our neurons firing efficiently, in addition to helping our immune system identify and destroy rogue cancer cells. When we load up on less-wholesome options, we miss out on the health-promoting foods.

Practicing flow in the kitchen makes it more likely that I will seize the opportunity to enjoy healthy food as often as possible, feeding myself and my loved ones really good healthy vegan food. That's a big part of my "why" now.

Practicing flow in the kitchen empowers me to live with integrity

Caring about the planet, the animals, and our own health is one thing. Living by those values, to me, means getting organized to prepare healthy food day after day. It's hard.

There are so many other commitments claiming to be more important investments and clamoring for my time and energy!

The first step of flow, as I will discuss in greater detail in the next chapter, is to assess the relative importance of those various commitments and channel our resources accordingly.

Once my priorities are set, I go through the weekly cycle of planning meals, getting food, batch cooking, daily cooking, and review. I have set times for each of those activities, just like I have set times for exercise.

To say "yes" to a healthy vegan way of eating, I have to set boundaries and say "no" to some other pursuits. Sometimes, it's yet another extracurricular activity that one of my kids would like to take on but that would dig too deep into my weeknight cooking time. At other times, it might be declining to serve on a committee that needs me as a volunteer. On those occasions when I go ahead and say "yes" to something new, I know it will involve some conscious compromise.

Do I need to be fully vegan to practice healthy vegan kitchen flow?

I became vegan just seven years ago. Though my palate has completely changed since, my heart and mind remember what life was like before I embraced a healthy vegan lifestyle. The pull of the traditions and conventions that make eating animal products seem natural, normal, necessary, and nice are very strong. Few people have the time and energy to explore and embrace new habits, especially if that puts them in conflict with loved ones and with society at large. I get it.

For those who are already (or mostly) vegan, avoiding increasingly abundant, convenient, and decadent food options in favor of wholesome homemade food also requires bucking powerful cultural and economic trends.

Yet, in the face of such powerful forces, even the smallest habit change can, over time, transform your life – and the lives of your loved ones, too.

Stick with me, learn a few tricks, and implement one of them in your life this week. See how it goes, then perhaps add another one.

Practice now

What's *your* why? Set a timer for 15 minutes and answer these two questions:

1) What motivates you to try practicing healthy vegan kitchen flow?

2) Visualize your days when practicing healthy vegan kitchen flow. What would it look like? How would you feel? How would your life be better?

Keep the sheet and post it in your kitchen, where you will be able to review your "why" at least once per week, or even every day.

Every few months, set a timer, do the exercise again, and update your answers.

CHAPTER 2

Conscious compromise

Most kitchen woes arise from neglecting the most critical part of our food lives: ensuring that our priorities and resources are in sync. The first phase of flow in the kitchen is to bring our full awareness not only to our food wishes but also to the means we can muster to make them come true. Only then can we effectively prepare to deliver upon the promises we make to ourselves.

Drawing insight from the practice of project management can help us make decisions about cooking. In the kitchen as on construction sites, scope, time, and cost must be kept in constant balance if we are to serve our loved ones really good food.

The project management triangle applied to home cooking

In construction, software development, and countless other industries, professional project managers are assigned to juggle the many people and things that must come in at just the right time. Their job is to deliver the best-quality product possible within the constraints imposed by money, time, and scope.

Scope reflects the specifications of the project: how big and complex the resulting product is supposed to be. A grandiose project, such as a hydroelectric power plant, requires a phenomenal amount of money and decades of work. A backyard shed can be built on a small budget over a weekend. But what if the scope shifts? If one wants to add intricate custom cabinets in the shed to accommodate a hobbyist' gear (scope creep), it will either cost more (hiring a professional for assistance) or take longer (as one learns the skills and does the work over several weekends). If suddenly the cost of materials skyrocket, the shed design will have to be simplified, or the budget will have to increase, or the total time to complete the project will stretch into the future, or all three. A good project manager understands the constraints and resources available and makes the best possible decisions — sometimes difficult ones — to make sure that what matters most isn't compromised.

In everyday cooking, although you may not have seen it that way before, there is also a project manager, even if they don't know their job title. Many of them go by the name "Mom" although dads, aunties, grandpas, and kids also can be in charge. Their ambition isn't to erect a skyscraper or update an operating system, but rather to keep their loved ones (and themselves) fed, perhaps even nourished. That's one of the most important jobs in the world!

Let's dedicate a few minutes to thinking about cooking as project management. What does the project management triangle mean when we apply it to our kitchen lives?

Scope

As the lead cook in your home, what are you trying to achieve? Are you aiming for 21 different home-cooked plant-based meals plus assorted snacks, all made only from whole foods every week? If so, that's a more ambitious set of specifications than simply "filling stomachs." For the latter, toast with peanut butter will do. For the former, you will need to invest more money (for kitchen appliances and ingredients) and more time (to learn and use knowledge and skills required to plan and execute).

Within the concept of scope, specifically related to vegan cooking, there are many dimensions to consider:

- Wholesomeness: Do you want to use only minimally transformed foods or are you okay with some level of processing? For example, is it important for you to eat only whole grains (like wheat berries), are you satisfied with whole-grain pasta, or is regular pasta perfectly fine to you?

- Variety: How many different foods and dishes do you want to eat at every meal, every day, and every week? Are you content eating the same breakfast every morning? Do you like a dinner that's composed of a spread of dishes, or are you fine with a one-pot dish like a hearty soup that contains everything in a single bowl?

- Freshness: Will you pull carrots from your garden right before dinner, buy produce from the farmers' market, use bagged carrots from the grocery store, or go for frozen or canned mixed veggies? Each level of freshness requires a different amount of effort.

- Presentation: Are you the styling type who fusses over the placement of basil leaves on top of your plate of spaghetti, or do you believe it's unimportant because "it all goes in the same place anyway?" How many different colors do you prefer to have on your plate?

- Environmental footprint: Do you want your food to come from within a 100-mile radius from your home? Trying to go zero-waste and plastic-free? Such requirements also add to the scope of your kitchen work.

Time

Cooking takes time. There's no way around it. So does cleaning. Every time you increase the complexity of the desired scope of your meals, you increase the number of bowls and kitchen tools that will need to be washed.

Planning meals and procuring ingredients also takes an amount of time that varies depending on the meals' specifications, and the knowledge and skills of the project manager. Deciding what's for dinner is a chore that can feel like a heavy burden, especially if the household's specifications are complex (allergies, picky eaters, etc.). Looking for recipes, if you feel you need them, takes time. Generating a shopping list from the desired selection of meals also takes time, as does going to stores, selecting ingredients, transporting them back home, and unpacking and storing them.

There's also the time needed to manage the kitchen inventory. When ingredients start to add up in the pantry and produce wilts in the fridge, the project manager must make some more decisions... or clean up the mess.

Money

If you live in a metropolitan area, and not in a food desert, basic ingredients are probably available at a reasonably low cost:

dry beans are cheap, whole grains reasonably inexpensive (if perhaps harder to find in some parts of town), and many basic yet nutritious vegetables like sweet potatoes and cabbage don't break the bank. If your specifications are strictly to cook up reasonably healthy meals without too much variety, it is possible to do so on a strict budget.

However, most of us have grown accustomed to a high variety of intensely flavored foods. This is perhaps truer for those who eat out a lot and have their pick from dozens of cuisines at every meal. In addition, processed and prepared food makers use many chemical tricks, including an enthusiastic embrace of salt and sugar, to enhance the taste of their dishes. Only about a third of Americans cook and eat at home every single day (for at least one meal). Most people, if served a dry bowl of quinoa, black beans, and mixed greens, will be underwhelmed.

The seasonings that add spice and zest to our meals are more costly than the basic ingredients. They are an up-front investment that can be intimidating for new cooks. Ready-made bottled dressings and sauces do exist but are generally much less healthy than their home-made counterparts... which require having a well-stocked pantry and cooking skills. Healthy options do exist, but they tend to be much pricier.

And then of course there are the appliances and the space available to store and manipulate foods. Those are some of the upfront costs that influence the possible scope of cooking in each home.

Bringing your priorities and resources in sync

Take a moment to consider your priorities when it comes to food, along with the resources you can realistically mobilize toward preparing the meals you want.

If you have high specifications, you will need to increase the amount of time and/or money you spend on ingredients and cooking.

We all have limited time, and most of us have limited money.

If you have lots of time, you can spend it learning how to make everything from scratch.

If you have lots of money, you can cut back on time by hiring help. (You'll need to account for the time you spend finding the perfect personal chef and giving them direction.)

If you are short on time and/or money, you need to adjust your specifications accordingly. You can still eat very healthy homemade vegan food, but you will benefit from learning to appreciate a simpler diet.

Keep in mind that, in building and technology endeavors, project managers can also harness the power of innovation. Similarly, you can learn new skills (knife skills, more efficient cleaning, better food storage…), try different cooking techniques, or discover a store where pantry ingredients are cheaper. Joining forces with others may also multiply your cooking power.

Practice now

What are your specifications for this week's meals?

What's critical? What would be "nice to have" but not exactly essential?

How much time and money can you realistically dedicate to preparing healthy vegan food for yourself and your loved ones?

Are there skills you can learn, different stores you can explore, or other innovations you can test to ease your practice?

CHAPTER 3

Why we resist cooking

The biggest enemy of flow in the kitchen is a bogged-down mindset.

When I ask people what stops them from cooking more healthy meals from scratch at home, I often hear some version of the following: "I hate cooking!" "Cooking feels like a waste of my time." "I'm sick of making dinner." "Why is it always me who's expected to know what's for dinner and somehow make it appear?" Dread and resentment abound.

I can relate because I, too, sometimes feel the same, often at about 5:47 p.m. on weeknights. Why is it that we hate cooking so much? I have some explanations to volunteer for that, along with suggested practices you can experiment with to find joy in cooking and start moving toward a state of flow.

Hate cooking? Blame capitalism.

What gets valued most in our contemporary capitalist culture is what makes the most money and boosts the Gross Domestic Product (GDP). Let's call that "production." On the flip side, we can call "reproduction" the love and effort that we put into nurturing the circle of life, from bringing and raising children into the world to caring for our elders. When it's done for free, that work isn't measured. Thus, it isn't valued within the capitalist system. It's just taken for granted that it happens.

From that perspective, home cooking is only valuable in as much as it helps sell cookbooks and magazines, kitchen appliances, microwave dinners, and other convenience ingredients and gizmos you'll want to buy because you think they'll make cooking better, easier, or faster.

There's one way cooking becomes economically valuable: it's when it is no longer done at home with love (by mom, for example) but instead outsourced to someone who is paid to do it. When that happens, reproductive work moves into the sphere of "production" and starts to "count." That's why restaurant food, meal kits, and all manners of "value added foods" (foods that have been prepared and processed to make them ready to eat or at least easier to prepare, as opposed to whole foods) are growing so steadily as a sector of the economy. The unfortunate coincidence is that they also steadily increase our waistline.

When we say, "I hate cooking," we mirror how we have internalized this devaluation of cooking as an act of service and love. When we eat industrially prepared meals, we give those economic forces further power to shape our bodies and minds.

Potatoes or value-added foods?

Think about potatoes. A farmer buys some seed potatoes, plants them, tends them, harvests them, and brings them to the farmers' market where you buy them to make mashed potatoes at home. That's a short economic chain with few opportunities for money to change hands along the way.

Now imagine adding "value" to the potatoes by combining them with other ingredients to create a packaged microwaveable dinner sold at a big box store. Those "convenient" products create many more opportunities for jobs, transactions, profit, and taxation. Bonus: whoever was cooking the potatoes previously (mom) can now work longer hours at a "real job" and earn a higher income.

In short, the most influential forces of our society benefit more when we don't eat healthy home-cooked meals. Incidentally, medical care for those suffering from diet-induced diseases also counts toward the GDP.

Isn't that an awful system?

We like to believe in ourselves as independent thinkers, but the truth is that it's very hard to be detached completely from those powerful undercurrents. Economic powers directly and indirectly shape our view through advertising and cultural products representing "normalcy." There are some counterforces in society, as evidenced by the fact that you are currently reading this book, but they are not as powerful.

We have reduced food to a transaction

Food to me is a sacred gift I offer myself and my loved ones. But outside of a handful of rebel kitchens and gardens, food has become the subject of just another transaction in our everyday life. It's nothing more than a commodity to be sold and bought. Buyers and sellers are only remotely concerned with food's nourishing qualities. We lose sight of the miracle that food embodies. We forget that it is nourishment born from a simple seed nurtured by sun, soil, water, and farmer.

Making matters worse, we have come to see food as the sum of a very limited range of individual, discrete nutrients. We weigh protein, carbohydrates, and fat, adding our "macros" and comparing ratios. We compute values for the few nutrients that we think we understand, most notably iron and calcium. Some believe that "a calorie is a calorie is a calorie."

Such a simplistic view of food leads us to believe that we know what we are eating when we read the label slapped on commercially available food. That's a profound delusion.

Our quantitative simplifications do not even start to reflect the complexity of food and nutrition. As highlighted in the books *Whole* and *The Future of Nutrition* by T. Colin Campbell (lead author of *The China Study*), every plant is an assemblage of thousands of different organic and inorganic chemicals, only a fraction of which we pay attention to. Despite decades of study, we have barely scratched the surface of an understanding of the interactions between them. We cannot yet fully appreciate how they transform from seed to harvest to fork, and how they are metabolized within the human body.

When we say, "I hate cooking" and expedite meals by filling ourselves with whatever calories we find most convenient to procure (and perhaps tasty to eat), we smugly ignore the complexity of nature. We fail to honor the miracle of life.

Mind the spiritual gap

Beyond the forces of biology, we also ignore the metaphysical dimensions of food. Hinduism in particular sees food as imbued with the spiritual energy that was put in it at all stages of its preparation.

Regardless of our religion (or lack thereof), we can appreciate the truly added value of preparing food as an act of love and service. For the cook, crafting a meal is an opportunity to be thankful for our lives, for the abundance of ingredients we get to choose from, and for the other beings we get to share the meal with. If nothing else, gratitude boosts our mood.

When we say, "I hate cooking," we deny ourselves this deeply soothing practice. When we cook with resentment and bitterness, we infuse the food with those negative feelings. When we put people who don't love us in charge of our meals, we put our bodies and souls at risk.

When not cooking is not a choice

The powerful economic forces that devalue food also devalue humans in general by casting us first as accessories for profit. Some of us have the resources and privilege to resist those forces and fight back with home cooked plant-based soup. Others, lacking secure housing with adequate cooking facilities, or exhausted from working multiple jobs to try and make ends meet, doubly suffer. First, they experience the indignity of being unable to cook their own food and share it with loved ones. Second, sooner or later, they also hurt from the painful consequences of malnourishment on their physical and mental health.

If we can easily access the resources to cook, but still say, "I hate cooking," we are wasting the gifts bestowed upon us. What if embracing a more nourishing way to live gave us the energy to share those gifts with those who need them?

Flip your mindset on cooking

If you have made it to this point, and still think you hate cooking, here is something you can do.

Instead of "I hate cooking," try saying: "Sometimes I hate cooking" or "Part of me hates cooking." "Hating cooking" is not who you are, it's not your identity! It's just how you feel at a certain moment.

Next, you can try saying: "I am learning to love cooking."

Or: "I am practicing making cooking feel better right now."

Think of it this way: you don't *have* to cook, you *get* to cook.

Observe what happens when you start to liberate yourself from the forces that want you to turn away from wholesome nourishment. Don't expect instant and perpetual success, but if you practice regularly, you will soon find yourself with a growing appreciation for this great act of love.

Conveniently, you get at least three opportunities to practice daily, at breakfast, lunch, and dinner. Get cooking and share the love.

Practice now

Reflect on how food has been valued throughout your upbringing and in your life today, from your closest circle (family and friends) to society at large. Talk to your parents or siblings about it if you can.

Give yourself grace for the times when you resist cooking, understanding that it is not a character flaw but the expected result of powerful forces beyond your reach.

Celebrate your efforts to break through the cultural molds and prepare to practice finding joy as you prepare healthy vegan food for yourself and your loved ones.

CHAPTER 4

To find flow, find joy

Though you may now understand how cooking became a de-valued burden in contemporary society, you may still dread it. Perhaps you resent it because you feel taken for granted as the default cook in your household. Maybe you think that you have more important things to do, or that cooking is beneath you.

Yet, can there be anything more important than carefully and lovingly preparing our food, since every cell of our bodies is made from what we eat? For that reason, I recommend that the person who cares the most about it should oversee cooking for the household. Might that be you?

If you're going to cook, you might as well do it with all your heart.

Not sure you can do it? Just pretend! Even if you are only going through the motions and act as if you enjoy cooking, you will start to experience some benefits. Keep on practicing and you will find flow.

Here are more than 20 practices you can play with to start making this critical task more pleasurable.

Nourish yourself first

When I talk with parents (especially moms) about their cooking woes, I so often hear them say how challenging it is to deal with their household's varied preferences and dietary restrictions. They are focused on catering to everyone's needs and often discouraged by some of the reactions they get from around the table. Indeed, many children and even adults are reluctant to embrace new foods or have a very narrow definition of what they consider "good" food.

When I ask them: "What's *your* favorite food? What do *you* want to eat?" they stare at me blankly. They haven't thought seriously about that in years. Time for a change.

I'm not saying that we shouldn't lovingly plan meals with picky eaters in mind, but cooking is like airplane safety. Just like we have to put our own oxygen mask on before assisting others, we need to nourish ourselves first to have the energy to nourish others.

You will find joy in cooking by thinking hard about the food that *you* want to eat and that will nourish *you*. Once you remember what you enjoy, make sure that your weekly meal plan reflects those preferences.

Cook only plants

When I decided to quit cooking animal products, including meat, dairy, and eggs, I felt a lightness about cooking I had not experienced before. I went down the road of plant-based cooking for environmental reasons but found a moral and ethical relief that I did not anticipate. I felt liberated to enjoy cooking in a way I didn't before. Recognizing that feeling guided me to become fully vegan when I was ready to do so.

Whether we recognize it or not, many of us have some awareness of the suffering that is embedded in animal products. Traces of the fear that pigs felt as they approached the kill floor remain in the bacon. As a mother, we may subconsciously perceive in our chest the suffering of the mother cow who lost her calf to the veal industry but still lactates. The hens' trauma of being born in a factory and seeing their brothers drop off the conveyor belt to their death is etched into the eggs they lay. When we cook the flesh and secretions of animals for our loved ones to eat, we are part of the chain of pain... and it hurts.

Cooking only plants liberates us from being complicit in this violent industry and creates a space where it is easier to find joy in cooking.

Joyful rituals

Create a ritual that brings you happiness, then practice that ritual every time you start cooking. As you do it every day, the association between "cooking" and "joy" will strengthen, allowing you to shed the "chore" vibes. Here are just a few examples of rituals you can adopt.

Play your power song

Choose one song that instantly picks you up and make sure to play it as you make your entrance into the kitchen. I have a sweet spot for *Happy* by Pharrell Williams but sometimes I need *Welcome to the Jungle*! If a jolt of energy is warranted before batch cooking, I love playing the theme song from Rocky loudly. If I'm baking (not my area of expertise), I may play Shakira's *Try Everything*.

Pro tip: create a playlist of favorite high-energy songs that will get you groovin' while cookin'. Think Nicki French's club version of *Total Eclipse of the Heart*, ABBA's *Dancing Queen*, or Jerry Lee Lewis' *Great Balls of Fire*. (My choices date me. You do you.)

If anyone complains, get yourself some wireless earphones as a present. It's cheaper than hiring a personal chef.

Energy reboot

Not into rock'n'roll? I've got something more chill for you. George Kao is my favorite productivity guru and I love his "Energy Reboot" ritual to get centered. It focuses our attention on love and gratitude. It's only a 30-second investment, which I suggest repeating with every new dish you cook to keep the joy fresh.

Here is how it goes, per George's own instructions:[3]

1. Breathe IN: love. I believe the universe is, in some mysterious way, actually made of love. We are literally breathing it in!

2. Breathe OUT: total security. I believe this is the real truth of your destiny and mine -- we have nothing to be afraid of; we will always be taken care of; we are headed inevitably toward ultimate bliss.

3. Breathe IN: guidance. Higher guidance is always available to us, let's open ourselves to it.

---

3   To learn more about George Kao's energy reboot practice, visit this page: https://www.georgekao.com/blog/energyreboot.

4. Breathe OUT: thank you. A natural response to higher Love and Guidance!

5. Breathe IN: joy. Connect to the joyful experience of this moment.

6. Breathe OUT: love and gratitude. I envision myself en-joying the next task I do.

   George does it as quickly as possible while keeping it meaningful, so that he is more likely to do it often.

As he says, "I get to do this thing that I'm about to do: what a privilege I have to get to become a better person through what I am doing now!"

Try it just once and see what how you feel.

Put on an apron

Dress up for cooking! Putting on an apron is a tiny ritual that helps us slip into our role as Loving Provider of Really Good Food. Bonus points if you have an apron that was worn by your grandmother or something fun that inspires you to cook healthfully.

One of my favorites is Dr. Michael Greger's "Cruciferocious" broccoli apron. Roar!

Say the cook's prayer

There are many out there, but I love this simple one:

"God bless my little kitchen, I love its every nook, and bless me as I do my work, wash pots and pans, and cook."

Mindfulness triggers

Thich Nhat Hanh, the Vietnamese Buddhist monk, suggested using red lights as mindfulness triggers when driving. Every time we see a red light, we can remember to be fully present in the moment. Why not apply this to cooking, too? Every time we see a light, we take a breath, and take in the sights, smells, sounds, and sensations of cooking. We can also take a bite and fully taste the food.

We can appreciate being alive and cooking really good food. There is a lot of joy to be found in that.

Choose whatever mindfulness trigger works well in your kitchen. Maybe it's every time you hear a beep, every time you pick up a knife, or every time you touch water, for example.

Write down a reminder to do this practice on a sticky note and place it where you will see it as you cook.

Create joyful associations

I would not want to be caught promoting multitasking, but if that's what required to get you cooking, why not? Reserve some activities you enjoy for cooking time only. Call your mom (wireless headset recommended), put on a favorite podcast, or enjoy a glass of kombucha while you cook.

Create a pathway in your brain that connects cooking with joy, making it a treat rather than a chore.

Gratitude

Repeat it like a mantra: "I don't have to cook this meal; I *get* to cook this meal." There are so many reasons to be grateful for this!

Changing that single word can help you find joy in cooking.

Play like a kid, observe like a scientist

When you start cooking a dish, consider it not as a test, but as an experiment.

You will *not* be rated on how closely your finished dish resembles the pictures from Pinterest!

You are setting out to use some ingredients and follow some steps and examine the results. Next time, tweak the ingredients and steps, and see what different results you get!

Do it with others: start a cooking club

Cooking used to be a far more social activity. Now that most of us live in single-family homes and apartments, we can feel quite lonely as we chop and stir.

Break down the kitchen walls (metaphorically!) by organizing or joining a batch cooking club with a few friends – or even with strangers from a local plant-based Facebook or Meetup group! Cooking with others on Zoom or another virtual meeting platform also creates community.

Do the littlest thing first

If you have a hard time getting started, consider taking even just a tiny step first. Think of it as a would-be runner who only commits to putting on their running shoes, giving themselves permission to abort the run if they still don't feel like it once they have their shoes on. Here are some equivalent tactics for the kitchen:

- Start warming a cast-iron skillet on medium-low heat.
- Add water to a pot and place it on the stove.
- Pick one spice or seasoning as "hero" for a dish you will now improvise.
- Chop an onion: (almost) every recipe needs an onion, so it won't be lost.

Still don't feel like cooking after doing one of those? Give yourself grace: you tried.

Or play the Rocky Theme Song and try again! (See "joyful rituals" above.)

High intensity interval cooking (HIIC)

You can do anything for 10 minutes, right? Set a timer and promise yourself that if you want to stop when it beeps, you're off the hook.

Even if you decide to keep going, though, don't power through without a break. "High intensity interval cooking" includes short breaks. If it works for fitness training, it might work for cooking, too!

Search for "HIIT timer app" in your device's app store. Get the simplest timer you can, then set a repeating interval: 10 minutes of intensity work (cooking), 2 minutes of break. You can even do shorter intervals to get started, like 5 minutes on and 2 minutes off.

During the 10 minutes "on," do nothing but cook with intensity and focus. In the 2 minutes "off," step out of the kitchen, shake your every limb, have a drink of water, and rest. (Don't pick up your phone!) Remember to turn off the burners before stepping out.

I bet you'll be eager to come back in and do the next 10-minute interval!

Embrace imperfection

It's cooking, not brain surgery.

It's OK to make mistakes.

It's OK if the dish doesn't look like those pictures the blogger posted on social media.

It's OK if not everyone likes it.

Unless you dropped the salt in the pot or totally burned the dish, it's quite fine to eat, even if it's not perfect.

Think back on the process, take stock of the results, wash the dishes, and live to cook another day.

Practice now

Now, pick one.

What will you do to infuse joy in your cooking next time you step into the kitchen?

Make a list of three to five tactics that appeal to you.

Write your list on a sticky note and post it on the most visible spot in your kitchen to remind yourself to get your flow going.

CHAPTER 5

The making of a healthy vegan meal

You now see why cooking really good food for yourself and your loved ones matters so much. You are ready to embrace the necessity of cooking with gratitude and joy as opposed to resentment. But... what are you going to eat?

Ideally, you would have a plan for your week's meals, and perhaps even have already cooked some of the building blocks. We will go into those two practices in depth in the coming chapters.

For now, let's focus our attention on the making of a single healthy vegan meal. This chapter is as much about optimizing nutrition (what you "should" be eating to feel nourished and satisfied) as it is about the process of cooking on weeknights.

Imagine this: it's 6:34 p.m. and you just got home. You are hungry. You don't have a previously cooked meal ready to reheat and gobble up. The temptation to pick up the phone and order something comforting from your favorite restaurant is high. But... wait! You know that, although tasty, that would probably not meet your standards. Delivery options tend to be expensive, wasteful, and not-so-healthy. You can do better at home – and it might even be faster.

In this chapter, I will show you the simple steps to improvise a balanced vegan meal from pantry ingredients – even when you are in no mood for cooking. You can do this! Once you take the first step, you'll build the momentum to keep on cooking.

Visualizing the process of improvising *one* healthy vegan meal, and starting to put your vision into practice, is the basis for planning multiple meals covering one or two weeks, which is the topic of the next chapter.

Pull out a knife and cutting board

A common piece of advice for those who need a nudge to get on with an exercise program is to go to sleep with their gym clothes on. When you wake up, you are already committed to starting your workout. The same is true when you need to commit to cooking: placing your cutting board on the counter and pulling out your favorite knife will get your cooking gears turning. Once your tools are laid out, wouldn't you feel ridiculous picking up the phone to order pizza?

Pro tip: Set your cutting board and knife out on the counter after putting away the breakfast dishes. It will be right there waiting for you to chop something when you come home at the end of the day.

If there is even the slightest chance that you'll be roasting anything, fire up the oven right away at 350 degrees Fahrenheit

(180 Celsius, gas mark 4). (But never leave the stove or oven unattended!) If you change your mind, just turn it off.

Pick your produce

Whether they are meal planning or improvising dinner, many omnivorous cooks start by asking themselves: "what protein do I have in the fridge?" By that, they mean meat. I get it: meat can be expensive, and it spoils quickly. When we start cooking plant-based meals, many of us carry that old habit over with us. We compose meals by asking ourselves what kind of protein-dense food we'll put at the center of the dish. "Tofu, beans, peas, seitan, or some kind of vegan meat?" That tends to be our starting point. Our meal planning process is driven by our undue obsession with protein. Even if we know that plants have protein, we can't shake our old pattern.

Let's flip that mindset over. The most precious food you have is fresh produce. Packed with micro- and macro-nutrients alike (including, yes, protein), colorful vegetables deserve the center stage of your meals.

In fact, the new Canadian Food Guide recommends that half the plate be occupied by vegetables – and they don't mean fried potatoes! To increase your odds of hitting the mark when you improvise a meal, go to your fridge and pull the fresh vegetables that are either just past their prime (but still edible!) or at their peak freshness. Cooked vegetables leftover from previous meals count, too.

If you do not have fresh or cooked veggies, look for a bag of frozen ones. Failing that, look for canned vegetables. Well done!

Getting started was the hardest part. Put what you found on the counter and move to the next step.

Choose the best-suited mode of preparation

Did you find crisp vegetables that will be best enjoyed raw (salad) or benefit from a quick meeting with high heat (stir-fry)?

Or did you dig out hard vegetables like roots or squashes that will best release their sugars in a simmered or roasted dish?

Perhaps all you have is slightly wilted produce or long-frozen vegetables that will modestly support a soup or stew?

Let whatever you found dictate your next steps, keeping in mind the urgency of your hunger. If you are already starving, roasting that head of cauliflower whole might not be the best strategy... but a quick chop into pieces will work.

If you have a good blender, keep in mind that many veggies also make a scrumptious sauce. Leftover cooked beets blended with some nuts (for creaminess) and a cup of pasta cooking water make an eye-popping hot pink sauce. Roasted orange sweet potato or squash, blended with a handful of nuts or seeds plus nutritional yeast, turns into a ridiculously healthy cheesy sauce — way better than anything you can get in a box (even the vegan version). If you found lots of wilting herbs in the produce drawer, you have the base for pesto.

Recruit supporting actors

Vegetables are the prima donnas of vegan dinners, but without protein-dense foods and (whole) grain ingredients, their show will leave you hungry for more.

Protein-rich foods

Beans, chickpeas, lentils, tofu, and vegan meats will combine just fine with any vegetable. But, if you have a choice, pick your cast based on the mode of preparation chosen above.

Your goal is to keep it quick and to avoid making too many dishes dirty.

If you're making a stir-fry, tofu and many meat analogs can be cooked in the same skillet as the veggies. I recommend sautéing them first, then setting them aside, sautéing the rest of the ingredients and adding the protein back in at the end, letting it all reheat for 2 minutes before serving.

If you are roasting things, then chickpeas spread on a baking sheet (perhaps tossed in a teaspoon of oil) will add a great contrast of texture to your meal. They'll be ready to eat at the same time as the veggies.

Lentils are best in soups and stews, although firmer ones (French "de Puy" green lentils and black beluga lentils) make great additions to salads, cooking while you're chopping the rest of the ingredients.

Make your protein choice and put the selected ingredient on the counter with the veggies.

Grains

For grains, I know pasta is an appealing option and I often reach for it myself. But remember that you can cook practically all other grains (and pseudo-grains like quinoa) the same way: bring a pot of water to boil, add the grains, and cook for 10-15 minutes (sometimes more), stirring regularly, tasting for doneness. Measuring isn't a requirement! When *al dente*, quickly drain through a fine-mesh strainer and return to the hot pot, covered, but off the heat. In 10 minutes, fluff with a fork and you're done.

Brown rice does take longer to cook than some other grains (22 minutes from the time it is added to boiling water to the time of draining). Red rice is faster (about 18 minutes depending on the variety). Cooking quinoa this way, you'll need to set a timer for 12 minutes (longer for red or brown quinoa).

Set the container of grains on the counter with the veggies and protein foods. The hardest part is behind you.

Start two fires...

Popular bloggers promise "one pot meals," and it does work in a limited number of cases (especially if you have prepped one of the meal components already). But the truth of dinner is that it is most often cooked in two pots: one pot for the grains, and a second pot (or skillet) for the rest. Another option is to cook the grains in one pot and to roast the rest. Or to throw the veggies to boil (or layer them in a steaming basket) in the same pot as the grains while using a skillet to enhance the texture of the protein.

Whichever way you go, you'll need two hot elements. The exception would be making soup, which can be done in a single pot.

Pause to think

Get your pots and/or oven going, then pause for a moment while they heat up. Look at what you have gathered on the counter. Close your eyes (just for 10 seconds!) and imagine what the finished dish will look like. You have eaten many meals in your life, so you don't need a photograph to tell you what to do.

Keep it simple.

Decide in what order things will be added to the heat. Denser ingredients take longer to cook, so make sure those get started as soon as possible. You don't need to know exactly what your plate will look like to get the yam halves started in the oven: you'll have plenty of time to think through details while they roast.

... unless you are making a raw salad.

I personally prefer my salads to have a cooked grain in them so I can feel really satiated, but if raw is your thing you may want to add spiralized root vegetables for the same purpose. Another option is to serve your big bowl of chopped and/or grated veggies with whole-grain crackers (like Wasa bread) or slices of a nice loaf of bread. In those cases, you won't need the fires.

Start cooking

Just because you aren't following a recipe doesn't mean you don't know what you are doing. If you have been cooking for yourself for more than a few months, you probably know a lot more than you think! You (roughly) know how to make a stir-fry, or soup, or stew, or fried rice, or bowl. (Refer to the appropriate section in the back of this book to refresh your memory.)

Just keep on cooking and trust yourself. If you keep the heat (from the stove and from chili peppers) and the salt in check, nothing terribly wrong can happen.

Your hands know what to do. Give them a chance to prepare the meal for you.

Finally: add flavor and nutrition boosters

Let's keep expectations in check: this is an improvised meal that you've hacked together at the last minute, without a plan, instead of ordering pizza. Whatever you do, it will be better for your health, for your pocketbook, and for the planet, than the alternative. If you can add a finishing touch to your dish, it will probably make it better for your palate, too! Here are some ideas to improve your creation:

- Add spices. Curry powder, taco seasoning, and other spice mixes you may have can be sprinkled onto your veggies as you cook them to add flair. Individual spices like cumin and smoked paprika are good on (almost!) everything. Add a little, taste, and add more if desired.

- Don't shy away from garlic and ginger. Those two are flavor bombs that also fight all the bad stuff in your body. Chop finely and add them to the pot during the last minute of cooking the vegetables, just before you add any liquid.

- Don't forget salt and pepper! If you are used to eating restaurant food a lot, you are most likely habituated to large amounts of sodium. It can completely change the experience of a dish. I certainly don't recommend that you try to reproduce that at home but be aware that your food will probably taste bland to you if you don't put any at all. Add a bit of salt during cooking, taste, and adjust seasoning. If you keep up the good habit of cooking at home, you can progressively lower the amount of sodium you consume.

- Scour your fridge and pantry for forgotten condiments

that can take your dish to the next level. Kalamata olives enhance the roasted vegetables from any Mediterranean dish. A spoonful of chutney will raise your curry's profile. What about a forkful of kimchi on that stir-fried broccoli?

Eat mindfully

Congratulations! The time has come to enjoy the fruit of your labor. Enjoy your dinner.

As you eat, pay attention to what's in front of you and how it feels in your mouth. Put words on the experience, asking yourself what you like about it. Think about what you would do differently next time. That's the best way to get better at improvising a meal.

Practice now

To increase your odds of improvising a healthy vegan meal at home next time you find yourself hungry, rehearse the steps above right now while they are fresh in your mind.

- Head over to your kitchen and open the fridge to identify the produce you would use.
- Pick your supporting actors (beans and grains).
- Visualize how you would cook it all together.
- Scan your pantry and fridge for flavor and nutrition boosters.

No need to cook the food for now! Simply running through the steps visually and mentally will do. Come up with at least 2 scenarios for healthy vegan meals you could improvise from what you have.

CHAPTER 6

Weekly meal planning as visualization

Dinner time is no time for decisions.

You now know the steps to improvising a balanced vegan meal, but you may not have started to use that knowledge yet. Putting it into practice at the end of the day, when you are feeling hungry or tired, may take you a long time or yield disappointing meals at first. You won't get to experience flow. Visualization techniques commonly used in elite sports can help you bridge that gap.

Cooking dinner for one's family isn't exactly a final dive at the Olympics' 10-meter platform, but still: the heat is on. To execute the feat fluidly and avoid a painful belly flop, you will benefit from having thoughtfully planned your act. Before it's time to start cooking, you will know that the dish you have chosen to make suits your skill level and your audience's specifications. You will have rehearsed the process in your mind ahead of time. Your body and mind will then be able to do what they were prepared to do — and cope with unexpected issues, too.

In this chapter, I will suggest a step-by-step approach to meal planning that you can practice every week. How long the process takes depends on your specifications (see chapter 2) and regularity. The more you go through the motions, and the more familiar you become with your constraints and ingredient options, the easier this phase will become.

But first, let's remind ourselves why meal planning makes such a difference.

Benefits of healthy vegan meal planning

Meal planning can seem like yet another chore, but it's an investment that pays off in many ways. Every minute you put into meal planning will save you at least three minutes in actual cooking time. In our busy lives, planning meals for the week gives us a much higher chance to:

- Eat a range of tasty and healthy food throughout the week.
- Feed our bodies and minds all the nutrients we need from a diversity of foods and ingredients.
- Save money (and our waistlines) by avoiding restaurants and convenience foods.
- Help save the planet by reducing waste.
- Make our families happy because we thoughtfully choose some meals that appeal to everyone's needs and preferences (or that can be adapted as needed).

- Have a (somewhat) peaceful meal because we're less stressed out by last-minute decisions and food preparation, especially if we are hungry and tired.

Meal planning is especially key for healthy vegan cooking, because there are fewer ready-made *and* healthy vegan food options available on store shelves.

Streamline healthy vegan meal planning in five steps

Meal planning does *not* start with asking Google for easy vegan dinner recipes or burying oneself under a pile of cookbooks.

Instead, grab a sheet of paper and divide it into the five weekdays, plus a section for the weekend. You can also use one of the templates from my website Vegan Family Kitchen. (See link on the last page of this book for a package of resources you can download.)

1. Take a hard look at your calendar

If you plan on making lasagna from scratch on the night when you are supposed to show up at a neighborhood town hall meeting at 7 p.m., I have some bad news for you: either the lasagna or the town hall meeting won't happen. Similarly, cooking a full meal from scratch immediately after 5 p.m. workout, when you are starving, isn't timely. Let's be realistic about the time and energy available for cooking, which probably varies from one day to the next based on schedule and commitments. Adjust cooking plans accordingly – revisiting chapter 2 on conscious compromises as necessary.

2. Create constraints by setting daily themes

The universe of healthy vegan food options is practically

infinite, thus choosing just a few meals for the coming week can be overwhelming. Setting constraints helps focus our attention.

Creating a framework for weekly dinners will narrow down the range of options and speed up decision-making. Common themes for plant-based vegan meal planning include things like "bowl day," "fun day," "taco Tuesday," "freezer day," "pasta day," etc. Another way is to be inspired by a different regional cuisine every night (Mexican, Indian, French...).

Pro tip: Since I buy groceries on Saturday or Sunday, I prefer to eat crunchy salads and stir-fries on Monday and Tuesday, leaving simmered dishes for later in the week. The themes can be the same throughout the year or rotate a bit with the seasons. Just keep it simple!

For weekend dinners, keep special events in mind, like visits with family and friends, and plan accordingly. In my family, Saturday night is often an improvised dinner designed to use as much leftover food as possible to make room for Sunday's batch cooking session. On Sundays, having done a prep session mid-day, the main cook (me) tends to get a break. We enjoy my mother-in-law's delicious plant-based cooking, eat out, or my husband cooks. Some flexibility keeps our healthy vegan way of eating sustainable over the long run.

3. Review your inventory

Looking back is just as important as looking forward when meal planning.

Open the pantry, fridge, and freezer. What's in there? Jot down a list of what is already in the kitchen, starting with fresh produce from last week and leftovers most likely to spoil soon.

If you find anything that's already past its prime, let go of your guilt and release it to the compost pile.

If there are leftovers that you can pull together to create a complete meal, slot that into a suitable space on your meal plan (sooner in the week rather than later).

Shine a spotlight on fresh produce you already have. Vegetables and fruits are the most valuable part of your food inventory, from both financial and nutritional points of view. Jot down specific veggies under suitable themes in your meal plan.

Take a deep dive into your pantry: anything interesting there? Zero-in on an ingredient that you haven't used in a while (or ever!) and think up a dish that could make use of it.

Don't hit Google in search of recipes! At least not yet.

Unless you started with an empty kitchen, you should already have at least one or two meals sorted by now.

4. Fill in the blanks

To complete your meal plan, choose some simple, classic meals that suit your themes. Customize them based on your inventory, the season (seasonal veggies are cheaper and often more nutritious), and your family's preferences. Take into consideration your commitments (soccer practice, committee meetings, etc.) to assess how much time you have available to cook on certain nights of the week. Plan accordingly.

I do not recommend following new recipes on weeknights. Instead, prepare by reading the explanations at the back of this book about how to cook standard healthy vegan dishes such as bowls and salads, stir-fries, soups and stews, and instant sauces. Start building your skills with the simplest possible version of those dishes.

Those cooking blueprints will also help you understand and modify conventional recipes better, should you decide to cook with them as a guide.

5. Complete your shopping list

Review every meal and jot down the ingredients you still need to buy to create your shopping list.

I know that, at this stage (or sooner), many will turn to Google or Pinterest to look for recipes for the various meals they've planned. Resist the urge! You know more than you think about cooking. I bet you can improvise a meal based on your experience.

Treat cooking like an experiment, notice the results, and repeat. If you find yourself missing an ingredient, just skip it! Or be creative about substitutions. The key is to pay attention to what's happening, cooking mindfully so you can apply the lessons learned next time.

Make sure to include items required for other meals (breakfasts, lunches, and snacks) on your grocery list.

Now get the groceries, block off the required time in your calendar to do it later, or place your order online.

Snap a pic!

Take a picture of your meal plan with your phone when you are done. You'll be glad to have it for quick reference at the grocery store, or for backup purposes if it gets lost.

What about breakfast and lunches?

Breakfast is my favorite meal of the day, yet the one I put the least thought into. My personal policy is to serve no more than two different breakfasts every week, from a very short list:

- Overnight oats with plant milk and seeds or nuts, plus fresh fruit. Sometimes, there's more chia seeds than oats. (See my website for more detailed suggestions to batch this.)

- Whole grain toast with nut butter and fruit (sliced strawberries or bananas, blueberries…) and a sprinkle of hemp seeds. If fresh fruit isn't available, my rhubarb-chia spread is a fantastic option. (I make lots in rhubarb season and freeze for later. Simply simmer the rhubarb, or fruit like strawberries or nectarines slices, until they turn soft and release a lot of their water. Add a few tablespoons of chia seeds to "gel" the mixture into a spread. Freeze whatever won't get eaten within a week.)

- Pancakes or waffles using my "whole everything" blender batter recipe. I make a big batch once or twice per week, and love freezing the extra for busy mornings. (Recipe is on my website – just search for "waffles.")

- Smoothies using frozen fruit and whole nuts or seeds (instead of plant milk), plus a pitted date or two, and one chunk of cauliflower if I happen to have some. My son will only have frozen fruit, so first I pour him a cup, then for the rest of us I fill at least half the blender with greens and top up with a bit more water and another pitted date.

For lunches, my husband and I always enjoy leftovers. A few times per week, we add a salad of dark leafy greens, some other vegetables (grated beets or carrots, finely sliced turnips, diced bell pepper… whatever is seasonal), some fruit if available, and a sprinkle of nuts or seeds, plus a splash of balsamic vinegar and maybe some olive oil.

On Saturdays before grocery shopping, I sometimes make a tofu scramble with everything that's left in the produce drawer. (I explain the process on my website. Search for "scramble.")

If you keep your pantry stocked and buy a little more fresh vegetables than required for your dinners, plus some fresh or frozen fruit, you will be able to cover breakfasts and lunches without a problem.

If you want to have more elaborate breakfasts or lunches, consider your conscious compromises again: would that mean that dinners will need to be simpler? (Revisit chapter 2 as needed.)

Working with seasonal produce

Finally, here is a good use for Google: search for "seasonal produce" followed by your region's name.

Produce in season is typically more nutritious and less expensive.

Spring is all about greens while summer produce is colorful, juicy, and thin-skinned. As we get deeper into fall, the vegetables get more fibrous and thicker-skinned. That's why spring is for salads, summer for stir-fries, and fall and winter for stews… though of course I eat those dishes most weeks, regardless of season.

Lovingly feeding picky eaters

If one or more chairs at your table is occupied by highly selective (a.k.a. picky) eaters, I want to say: "thank you for trying." It can be a very difficult and thankless task. Though you cannot see it today, your efforts will make a difference in that person's life over the long term and in how they show up in the world.

In this book, I will not go in depth about this topic – you can read more about it on my website or watch the replay of my workshop on the topic. Still, I wanted to provide a few tips to deal with the frustration and accompany your diners on their food discovery journey. I refer to "your child" but most of this would also be valid for an adult who is reluctant to embrace new plant foods.

Make three lists

Take a moment to reflect on the last few months of eating and try to see the world through your child's eyes. Create three lists: one with their favorite foods (the "green" list), one with the foods they will eat (even if they are not their favorites), and finally one with the foods they have no interest in trying (the "no-no list"). It helps to do this with your child, as it will make them feel empowered and engaged about their meals.

Including safe foods with every meal

For every meal in your upcoming week's meal plan, include at least one safe ingredient (from the first list) two if possible. Those should be foods they will eat without reservation. Go for the healthiest ones or try to modify them subtly so they at least approach your standards. Make sure there is enough of it so that they do not feel like they will starve.

As much as possible, those should be ingredients that also belong in the main dish that the rest of the family will eat, so you can highlight how children and adults eat the same thing. For example, if I am making a Buddha bowl for the family, I set aside some plain tofu and unseasoned quinoa. Or, if making chili, I set plain beans aside.

I suggest planning no more than one or two meals per week with foods from the no-no list, if possible.

Let friends introduce friends.

Serve new foods alongside trusted old favorites to increase their likelihood of facing at least a lukewarm welcome. Plan to add one new ingredient to a recipe from your child's list of favorites. If the change is drastic, you can start with just a small portion, making sure to keep most of the dish "untainted."

Schedule happy meals

Make sure to schedule at least one meal from the green list every week. It conveys the message: "Mom/Dad loves me and prepares food I enjoy." If the list is very short, it can get boring for adults, but it is useful for the grown-ups to eat a recognizable version of the kids' food occasionally… while also visibly enjoying a side dish that would stretch the picky eaters' boundaries.

Never force them to take a bite… but what about a sniff?

Whatever you do, never, ever force them to eat something. Every study done on picky eating has repeated it: forcing a child to eat a food they find repulsive – even "just a little bite" – will backfire and lead them to hate it even more. Such food aversions can last long into adulthood and ruin perfectly great vegetables needlessly. Nobody builds happy food memories and positive associations when forced to put something in their mouth and swallow it. Eating out of spite when assailed by hunger pangs isn't better.

Nevertheless, your picky eaters may be gently talked into engaging into foreplay with foreign foods. Encourage them to touch and smell the food. All clear? What about a lick? No need to make a big deal of it, but if your child is curious, they may play along. Maybe they won't go as far as taking a bite today, but next time the food shows up at the table, it won't be as a stranger.

Mutual respect

We teach our children that their bodies belong to them and that they can say "no" if they don't want someone to hug or kiss them. Then why would we make them *eat* something? They are the masters of their bodies and should be respected as such.

As the cook who toiled in the kitchen to prepare the meal, we deserve respect too. We certainly shouldn't take their reluctance to eat the food we make personal. However, we can teach them how to express it politely.

Instead of "I don't like this" or "this is yucky," try teaching your child to say, "I don't want to eat this now." It helps if adults model this behaviour.

Not only does this phrasing protects the cook's ego, but it prevents the child from growing up thinking that disliking a certain food is part of their personality, part of who they are. Don't let them think: "I am the kind of person who doesn't like broccoli." Aim for "I don't feel like broccoli tonight." Tomorrow is another day.

Good luck!

Save more time: do it two weeks at a time

After practicing weekly meal planning for a few weeks or months, you are ready to double up: plan your meals two weeks at a time.

There are many benefits to planning 10 to 12 dinners at a time instead of just 5 to 7:

- The most challenging thing about meal planning can be getting yourself psyched to start. You're saving yourself that step by doing it every other week only.

- No need to revisit your seasonal produce chart; things don't change much from one week to the next.

- You can cook extra big batches of whole grains and beans, then mix and match over several days. Whatever won't be eaten within the first week can be frozen for the next.

- Most dressings and many sauces are fine in the refrigerator for two weeks.

- Many dishes can be transformed across multiple dinners. For example, a big pot of slow cooker chili can be served on brown rice one night and rolled into burritos a few days later.

- Toppings can also be included in different meals: nutty cream makes a fabulous chili topping one day and turns into an instant sauce for creamy pasta with roasted vegetables another night.

- Most vegan dishes and components freeze perfectly, including spreads like hummus and pesto, meat alternatives like seitan, sauces, etc. But don't forget them in the freezer! Having a plan to use them in the next month or so will prevent food waste due to freezer burn.

- Once you create a 2-week thematic plan you like, you can simply repeat it, with slight changes in the produce choices or different grains and legumes.

Too much to think about? Get your meal plans done for you instead.

If you are new to the world of plant-based cooking, the breadth of unfamiliar options may overwhelm you at first. Or maybe you are just busy and suffering from decision fatigue. In that case, you may benefit from subscribing to a meal planning service.

There are two main types of meal planning services to choose from:

Curated meal planning services use bots to harvest thousands of recipes from the Internet, put them in a database, and tag them based on various attributes like common dietary requirements (vegan, dairy-free, gluten-free, etc.), mode of preparation, time of day, etc. Some services work from an extensive database of their own recipes or put more resources toward modifying recipes to fit their style, taking fresh photos, etc. With varying degrees of human intervention, you receive a weekly meal plan that reflects your preferences, including the recipes and a compiled shopping list.

Hand-made meal plans contain purpose-created recipes designed specifically for the needs of their subscribers. They tend to reflect the style and personality of the lead chef for the service. In the case of the service I offer, the Vegan Family Kitchen's Vegan Meal Plans, the focus is on healthy vegan cooking using mostly whole foods, increasing efficiency by using similar ingredients across recipes and "cook once eat twice" dishes, and reducing food waste. My plans cover two weeks' worth of meals at a time as I have found this approach to be most efficient. They rely on batch cooking sessions during the weekend to cut back on weeknight cooking time and stress. Subscribers receive recipes, shopping lists, and pre-determined prep steps, so they don't have to "deconstruct" their meals into building blocks on their own.

Meal planning services include access to customer service agents (in my case, myself!) available to answer your questions should you struggle to understand the instructions, find it difficult to secure some of the ingredients, or need to make substitutions due to allergies, for example. I can't speak for the other services, but I know that I am personally committed to responding to even the most basic questions with love and as quickly as possible because I am dedicated to helping more people eat more plants (and fewer animals).

By following the meal plans — mine or others — to cook your meals, you will further build your confidence and skills while decreasing the amount of both food and packaging waste, to say nothing of the money you'll save. Plus, you'll learn to customize the plans and recipes to suit your needs, growing into an independent home cook.

Practice now

Let's plan your meals for next week.

First, revisit your "why" as posted on the fridge (see chapter 1) to remind yourself why you are putting in love and effort into this.

Then, download one of the templates from my website (link at the back of the book) or just draw boxes on a sheet. You should have spaces for:

- Inventory: items you already have and plan on using.
- Each of the five weekdays.
- The weekend.
- Breakfasts and snacks (one box for all).
- Lunches, if you plan on eating anything other than leftovers (one box for all).

Review your calendar and commitments to create realistic expectations about your time and energy available for cooking on weeknights.

Set themes for each night.

Review your inventory and start filling in the spaces.

Add a few meals based on standard dishes, using seasonal vegetables.

Create a shopping list accordingly and commit to a time to get groceries.

Snap a picture of your meal plan for reference.

Take a deep breath and head out to the supermarket, with gratitude for your ability to access nutritious, delicious plant foods.

CHAPTER 7

Batch cooking to save lives

Batch cooking changes lives... it really does! In fact, healthy vegan batch cooking also *saves* lives. Why? Because when you have got a meal ready to eat in the fridge or freezer, you are much less likely to eat unhealthy processed or delivery food (saves human lives!) or revert to eating easier-to-prepare meat (saves animal lives!).

Flow favors the prepared

Healthy vegan cooking is not more difficult, but for those of us who have been raised as omnivores, it might not come quite as naturally. Plus, I also found out that googling the phrase "quick dinner recipes" yields mostly meat-heavy recipes with practically no vegetables. Not good! To make it easy to stay on the path of eating varied, healthy, delicious, and plant-based meals, without starting to cook dinner at 3 p.m. every day, you need to get organized. A regular healthy vegan batch cooking habit is what you need! Thanks to weekend batch cooking, your fridge will be filled with really good food.

Batch cooking vs. meal prep

Haven't we all watched with envy as some YouTuber prepped 30 meals in 30 minutes, all in matching containers neatly stacked in the fridge? That's what I call meal prep. Although I acknowledge the appeal of such a practice, it does not work for my family, mainly because we don't enjoy reheated food and repetition much. It's fine for leftovers at lunch, but when I eat a meal for the first time, I want it to feel and taste fresh.

I prefer cooking some of my meals' building blocks on the weekend, so they are ready to deploy on weeknights. For example, I might mix dressings, cook up a big batch of brown rice, or slow cook a two-bean chili. When it's time to assemble the dinner, I just toss some fresh greens together, cook noodles, or create a quick spread of taco toppings, in addition to reheating the main part of the dish.

An added benefit is that the flavors of many simmered dishes are enhanced by a day or two in the fridge, so weeknight meals taste even better than if I had cooked everything from scratch right before dinner.

I call that practice batch cooking. The practice also refers to making huge batches of things like chili or spaghetti sauce and freezing them for later. That's also part of my weekend batch cooking sessions, since many building blocks can be cooked once and eaten twice or thrice. (See my suggestion to plan meals two weeks at a time in the previous chapter.)

This strategy requires that you set aside an hour or two on the weekend to do a little batch cooking. Your first time, it might take three hours, but you will soon become more efficient. You will be amazed at what you can do in just 60 minutes... if you are focused.

Make a commitment that reflects your priorities

Eating better, and cooking more healthy vegan meals at home, is a great idea in theory. In practice, if this is a new habit, it will require more than a collection of vegan batch cooking recipes to make room for the extra cooking time. We need to know in our heart of hearts that it is important to us and know why. We need to decide that it is a priority for us to feed ourselves and our loved ones more whole food plant-based meals cooked at home, mostly from scratch.

Maybe eating this way is something you're thinking about, but you have other more pressing issues you feel you need to deal with now. That's OK. But if you do decide that cooking better to eat better is a top priority, then you need to make space for the required actions in your life.

Are you still with me?

Make it fit into your life

Now, before you hit the kitchen, take a step back and think about your life. Consider your obligations and schedule, along with the upcoming commitments on your calendar. Now is a good time to revisit your anchor (chapter 1) and conscious compromises (chapter 2). Ask yourself some deep questions:

- What are the most important food values to me? Whole foods, home-made, affordable, zero-waste, varied?

- How important are those food values relative to other aspects of my life that require my time?

Then, make choices accordingly. Let's think of a few examples:

- If whole foods and plant-based are your top priorities, affordability is not a concern, and you have other pressing priorities in your life, maybe hiring a personal chef is a better use of your time than trying to do batch cooking on a regular basis. (Good for you!)
- Maybe you care a great deal about whole foods but have very little time and money to dedicate to food. Then you'll probably need to simplify and decrease the variety of the meals you prepare. Make judicious, nutritious choices of dishes, cook big batches of them, and eat them multiple times per week/month.

Knowing your priorities will help you create a wise batch cooking plan.

Decoupling cooking from dinner

Let's get practical. Look at your planner or calendar and ask yourself some questions:

- How much time do I have for cooking at mealtime on a daily basis?
- Can I dedicate minutes or hours to cooking at times other than typical mealtimes? How much and when?

Be realistic! Maybe in theory you think you have an hour for cooking after picking up the kids from school, but in practice they are starving by the time you come home and if you don't have a plan to feed them right away all hell will break loose. You better have either a nutritious snack available (calming their hunger without filling their tummy) or be ready to put dinner on the table. Either way, you need to plan (and cook) something ahead or else revert to food out of a box. Those are your priorities in action.

When exactly can you cook? Once you have decided, block the time in your calendar just like you would for a dentist appointment, work meeting, or workout.

Tip for families: If you are lucky enough to have a partner or older child who can take charge of putting dinner on the table, factor them in (along with their schedule).

Find the right schedule for you

Keeping your priorities in mind, block some time on your calendar to cook. If you have a carefully designed meal plan, you can probably get away with 15 to 30 minutes on weeknights and two, maximum three hours on the weekend. When is that going to be?

Don't forget to make time for grocery shopping! Put that in your calendar, too.

Deconstruct your meal plan into building blocks

Unless you have excellent improvisational cooking skills, and a perfect track record when it comes to managing your fresh produce inventory, I don't recommend starting batch cooking before having created a meal plan (see previous chapter).

Look at what you jotted down for the coming week. Then, apply a modular lens to your meal plan and deconstruct every meal into its building blocks.

For example, let's say the planned dinner is "spaghetti with vegan Bolognese sauce." That meal has two essential building blocks: the pasta and the bolo sauce. Pasta is quick to make, but home-made vegan Bolo-style sauce with lots of veggies requires more work. Plus, like most simmered dishes, its flavors will develop if a couple of days elapse between cooking and eating. That makes it the perfect candidate for weekend batch cooking, or at the very least weeknight double-batching (cooking double or triple the amount you'd normally eat and freezing the extra).

If you make the sauce ahead of time, you'll just have to reheat it when dinner time comes. That way, you will enjoy its delicious and nutritious contribution to your meal with no weeknight effort. You can use the remaining time to toss a quick salad of mixed greens and fresh veggies... or read a book.

Keep your gear and space in mind

Get started with what you have. Don't wait until you have just the right equipment.

How many pots can you use at the same time? Are there two shelves in your oven? Do you have an electric pressure cooker (Instant Pot)? Can you borrow a slow cooker from your neighbor just to try it out? What about your containers - will you have enough to store the cooked food? Is there space in your fridge?

To keep cleanup time in check, avoid using multiple small appliances every week. For example, choose recipes that make use of your blender one week, and for the next week choose food processor recipes. It will streamline your cleanup time.

Before starting a big batch cooking session, wash any dishes that may clutter your sink and clear your countertops. You'll be so much more efficient! And less likely to injure yourself.

And don't forget the labels! Unidentified food is more likely to end up wasted.

Be strategic about your batch cooking time

Start your session with items that take a long time but are relatively hands-off. For me, it usually means cooking a gigantic batch of brown rice (takes about an hour but hardly any hands-on time) and roasting vegetables.
Save the light tasks, such as mixing dressings, for last.

Keep cleanup in mind: if using a blender for a few different items, start with dry or light-colored mixes. For example, I always make cashew cream before pesto. That way I don't even have to rinse the blender: leftover cashew cream just makes my pesto more delicious!

Some examples of building blocks for batch cooking

- Whole grains and pseudo-grains like quinoa, brown rice, barley, wheatberries, farro, couscous, etc.
- Soups (without noodles) and stews including chilis and curries
- Sauces like marinara and vegan Bolognese
- Simmered and seasoned beans
- Bean spreads like hummus
- Vegan burgers, meatballs, and loaves
- Pizza dough
- Roasted vegetables
- Lasagnas and enchiladas
- Dressings
- Pesto
- Hearty salads including chickpea, potato, and others

Practice now

Create your batch cooking plan based on the meal plan you created in the previous chapter, identifying the building blocks that can be prepared ahead of time.

Decide on the time when you will be doing your batch cooking session. You should plan for one and a half to two hours of focused cooking, plus the final clean up. Beyond that, fatigue and distraction may stretch the process to the point of diminishing returns. If your list of building blocks is too long for a two-hour session, revisit your conscious compromise. Make sure you have all the supplies and ingredients you will need.

Then: DO IT.

CHAPTER 8

Start with the minimum viable prep

Did the previous chapter about batch cooking intimidate you? There is an alternative: the Minimum Viable Prep (or MVP). It might very well become your most valuable practice to facilitate flow in the kitchen.

Eating unprocessed, home-cooked plant-based meals every day takes more time than dishing out processed foods from a box. (Duh!) It doesn't have to take a prohibitive amount of time: four to seven hours of cooking per week should yield very enjoyable meals.

If you cannot see yourself cooking for that amount of time every week, it is still possible to enjoy delicious, home-made healthy vegan meals. However, you may have to compromise on food diversity. It's not a dream dinner scenario, but you can get by with what I call the minimum viable meal prep. To feed a single person or a couple, it requires about one hour on weekends and a few minutes every weeknight.

Take these basic steps on the weekend and you'll have some healthy vegan options available on weeknights when you have no time to cook.

What if you don't have time for even basic batch cooking?

Before I proceed with my suggestions, I want to acknowledge something. Not everyone has "weekend" time to cook. Many of us work long hours, most days of the week, or multiple jobs, to make ends meet. Others are committed to caring for loved ones in a way that detracts them from caring about their own health. The obstacles to eating better dinners are, for some, insurmountable.

This said, many of us are also just plain busy. We have said "yes" to a lot of important and interesting engagements, for ourselves and for our loved ones, without considering our other priorities, like eating nourishing food so we can thrive.

If you think you have no time at all to do even basic plant-based batch cooking on some less-busy days of the week, I invite you to reconsider your schedule and perhaps say "no" to an activity or two. Or delegate responsibilities to others.

If work is the problem, ask yourself: what is the full, real cost of working more hours? Again, I am not talking to those who are scraping by at the edge of survival here. If the increased stress and busyness make it impossible for you to cook at home from scratch, then you are likely eating more processed food or buying ready-made meals. Perhaps you buy groceries in hopes of preparing a series of delightful dinners but end up wasting most of that food (and money) because it spoils before you cook it. In addition, the long-term costs of eating an unhealthy diet with too much fat and sodium, and too many calories, include years of decreased quality of life, a costly medication regimen, and overwhelming health expenses. For what?

Take a hard look at your life. Can you claim an hour to do this basic healthy vegan batch cooking at some time during the week and follow through with 15 minutes of dinner prep every night?

If so, here's how to implement it.

Pick your plant-based basics: beans and grains

Legumes and whole grains form the backbone of healthy vegan nutrition. Both have fiber and protein, as well as many of the micronutrients we need. Although it is technically possible to thrive without them, busy people will need to rely on them for most of their daily nourishment. And that is great, because they are both diverse and delicious! Both categories should be represented in your basic vegan batch cooking plan.

Pulses: This category includes beans, lentils, chickpeas, split peas, edamame, and their derivatives, such as tofu (a minimally transformed soy product). There are so many options, just make sure you always have a few in stock. Choosing a dark-colored bean (black beans, kidney beans, etc.) will also increase the phytonutrients you get in every bite, compared to white beans and chickpeas. But chickpeas are delicious, so just make sure to mix things up from week to week. If you are starved for time, I won't suggest that you cook your beans from scratch. Dry beans are cheaper but if you have only minutes to spend on your meals, they are not the best investment of your time. Get canned beans.

Grains: Think beyond the wheat! Yes, pasta is delicious. So is bread. But you can prep something more wholesome and nutritious in mere minutes. Pick a whole grain or pseudo-grain, whether it's brown or red rice, quinoa, barley, farro, buckwheat, millet, or freekeh. Follow package instructions or learn about my easy fuss-free methods for rice and quinoa (see "Cooking whole grains" section of Part Two). If you are pressed for time, couscous is practically instant and can be found in a whole-wheat version.

Roast the oranges

Root vegetables and winter squashes are inexpensive and robust veggies that you can keep for several weeks in your produce drawer. The red and orange ones are particularly good sources of carotenoids critical for eye health. Roasting enhances their flavor while improving the availability of their nutrients. Plus, the hands-on time requirement is very short.

My top choices are orange sweet potatoes (so-called yams), carrots, and red onions. They are particularly awesome because they require minimal preparation before roasting and deliver a big nutritional punch in addition to rich flavor. Sweet potatoes and carrots just need a thorough brushing, no need to peel! Onions do need to have their outer skin removed of course, but it's a quick job.

Chopping the veggies in thumb-sized pieces will do. Spread on a baking sheet lined with parchment paper (to speed up cleaning), sprinkle with salt, pepper, and turmeric (if available), and maybe drizzle with a little olive oil. You're good to go.

Many squashes do not need to be peeled, either, but if you choose to do it, it's easier to do so after they have been roasted. Either way, you have to start by halving them and removing the seeds and fibrous bits. You can roast them just like that, cut face down on a lined baking sheet. Roasting halves will require more time in the oven than dicing. If you forget them in the oven too long, you'll get to scoop out ready-made squash purée: lovely!

Get the greens

I am all for zero-waste, but if you are short for time, you have my blessing to buy a convenient box of pre-washed boxed or bagged greens. Choose the "baby" option like kale, or so-called "power greens" which are usually a mix of different nutritious young dark leafy greens. Those provide maximum nutrition for minimum effort.

A more economical and eco-friendly option is to buy a bunch of kale, rinse it in plenty of water, rip the leaves off the stems, then chop into ribbons. (You can slice the stems finely and add to soups or stews at the same time as the onion.) Massage the leaves energetically (to break down the tough fibers) before storing in a container with a paper towel or cloth napkin at the bottom (to prevent them from getting soggy).

Add a soup or stew

Soups and stews are the ultimate prep-friendly dishes for your basic plant-based batch cooking session. You don't even need a recipe to improvise a tasty soup or stew with lots of flavor.

(If you have never done it, there's guidance at the back of this book. See the "Soups and Stews" section.) And you don't need to worry about chopping things nicely if you plan on blending everything smooth at the end. Prefer it chunky? Call it "rustic" and you're done.

Make the most of your time

Recap: you have four things to do in your minimum viable meal prep: cook grains, roast orange vegetables, get greens ready, and prepare a soup or stew. Here's the exact order I suggest you do it in:

1. Start the oven at 375 degrees Fahrenheit (170 Celsius, gas mark 5).
2. Fill a big pot halfway with water and set on the stovetop on high heat.
3. Rinse the grains in a fine-mesh strainer and set aside.
4. Chop the orange vegetables for roasting and put them in the oven for about 40 minutes. If you remember to flip them partway through, great, but it doesn't matter that much.
5. In a heavy pot on the stove on medium-low heat, start cooking your soup or stew by sautéing the onions for a few minutes. It will make them extra sweet and flavorful.
6. Keep an eye on the pot of water. When it boils, add in the grains. If it's brown rice, cook for 22 minutes. For other grains, taste often and use your judgement. (See "Cooking whole grains" section in Part Two for more detailed instructions.)
7. Keep on adding veggies to your soup or stew, cooking each for two or three minutes before adding the next.

Add in the rest of the ingredients and simmer until everything is cooked to your liking.

8. Your grains should be ready at some point during the simmering of the soup. Drain through the fine-mesh strainer, return cooked grains to the hot pot, cover, and let it all rest for about 10 minutes, off the heat. The grains will finish steaming. Fluff them with a fork.

9. The orange vegetables should be done roasting by now. Take them out of the oven.

10. Make sure you have some greens. If they come pre-washed in a box, there is nothing else. If you are using bunched kale or bulk greens from the farmers' market, rinse and spin them clean. Massage that kale! Store in airtight containers or bags, with a paper towel at the bottom to absorb extra moisture.

11. Transfer everything to labelled containers and refrigerate. Some people like to pre-assemble bowls and divide their meals into portions. If you're on the go a lot, that may be a good strategy for you.

Jazz it up with tasty and nourishing pantry staples

Make sure to stock some of the following to add into your meals once you assemble them:

- Nuts and/or seeds (almond, walnuts, pecans, pumpkin seeds, hemp seeds, sesame seeds, sunflower seeds...)
- Nutritional yeast
- Dried fruit (raisins, unsweetened cranberries, currants, apricots...)
- Balsamic or fruit vinegar (visit your supermarket's "fine foods" section)

- Lemon or lime juice (keep refrigerated)
- Frozen mango and frozen avocado (mix together with a pinch of salt and maybe lime juice for a fantastic topping for curry or chili)

How to eat all this

You now have beans (from a can), whole grains, roasted orange vegetables, greens, and a soup or stew. Here are some combinations to inspire you.

Compose vegan bowls

Scoop of grains + scoop of beans + scoop of orange roasted veggies + handful of greens + extra veggies if you have them (cherry tomatoes, a grated carrot or beet…) + extra antioxidants from fresh berries or dried fruit + sprinkle of nuts or seeds + splash of lime juice or fancy vinegar. Voilà: vegan bowl from your minimum viable prep.

Stir(-fry) it up

If you have the extra 15 minutes, you can make what looks like a different dish by heating up the wok or skillet and making a "fried rice" style dinner. Your veggies are already cooked, so start with about half of the grains you plan on eating, sautéing them around the hot skillet until heated through. You can use a teaspoon or two of oil or vegetable broth to sauté. Add the beans and roasted veggies, sauté again until warm, then the rest of the grains. Throw in a handful of greens and a splash of lime juice or soy sauce. When everything's piping hot, you are done!

Just heat up that soup or stew

Those soups and stews make amazing lunches because you can just warm them up in the microwave. They'll also be very comforting at 9 p.m. after a long day of work when you haven't yet had dinner. Sprinkle with nuts and nutritional yeast or add a spoonful of your favorite salsa or chutney.

Stuck in a rut?

The minimum viable prep blueprint I have just drawn for you is very basic. It's nourishing enough... but after a few weeks you might lose interest. Here are some tricks to shake things up.

Roast seasonal vegetables: Instead of sweet potatoes and squash, try a new, seasonal vegetable. Asparagus is only available locally in the spring, so don't miss it! Radishes, zucchini, and mushrooms are also great when roasted, just combine them with the orange veggies. When cauliflower is on sale, grab one!

Freezer strategy: Get in the habit of doubling up your grains and soup or stews, so you can freeze half for later. Make sure to label the containers well and keep an inventory sheet on the fridge to remind yourself of what's available.

Add-ons: As you get more skilled and faster at this basic plant-based batch cooking thing, I recommend you add a couple of other basics to your meal prep plan, like sauces, dressings, and spreads you can use for sandwiches. See section on "instant sauces" in Part Two for ideas.

Practice now

Is the minimum viable prep for you? Or do you need to eat five or more different dinners every week?

Revisit your "why" (chapter 1) and think back upon your conscious compromise (chapter 2).

If you want to try the MVP, customize the steps to your needs, deciding on:

1. What grains you will prep.
2. What vegetables you will roast.
3. What greens you will select.
4. What soup or stew you will cook.
5. What bonus ingredients you have to jazz it all up, and which ones you need to buy.

Set a date and time for your minimum viable prep and DO IT.

CHAPTER 9

Cooking mindfully

Having carefully planned our meals and strategically decided on our batch cooking goals, it is now time to step into the kitchen to make really good food. Let's cook!
And only cook.

At a time when kitchen appliance companies are building voice-operated smart tablets into fridges and stoves, the advice in this chapter puts me at risk of coming across as curmudgeonly. Yet, in the face of the irresistible pull of technologies that compete for our attention and consumer data, I dare you to attempt a courageous act of resistance: kick smartphones, devices, and computers out of your kitchen, and practice mindful, screen-free cooking.

Your flow in the kitchen depends on it.

Reclaim your attention and autonomy

Before we dig into cooking specifically, let's take a step back and think about our digital devices more generally. Our phones and tablets, as well as the apps they are running, are designed and built to make it more attractive for us to spend more time using them. In fact, they are designed to be addictive: a former Google employee has coined the expression "a slot machine in your pocket" to describe our phones. In the attention economy, the most valuable commodity isn't gold, but every minute your eyeballs spend staring at a screen. Many of the platforms we use, such as Instagram and YouTube, appear to be free to us, but that's because *we are the products*. For every minute we spend scrolling down our feeds or watching video, online media companies can show us more ads — and make more money.

Obviously, it's working. The average American spends nearly four hours using a mobile device every day, and for younger people it's about twice that, or more. Many of us spend half of our waking lives actively using mobile devices. It's suiting that half of the world's biggest companies (measured by market capitalization) are those commandeering the online space: Apple, Microsoft, Google, Amazon and Facebook.

In his manifesto *Digital Minimalism: Choosing a Focused Life in a Noisy World*, computer scientist and author Cal Newport reviews the deep implications of our mindless use of connected devices. He highlights how the small benefits we may gain from constant device use are dwarfed by the overwhelming tide of digital clutter that invades our life in return.

When it comes to cooking, the trade-off isn't any more beneficial: phones and tablets in the kitchen slow us down and dumb us down too. Newport's solution of a "30-day digital declutter" may be too radical to many of us. But can I perhaps convince you to try a one-week kitchen cleanse to start? No special juices to drink! Just keep your screens out of the kitchen and observe what happens.

Do you really need to follow the recipe?

The number one reason why people say they want to bring their devices into the kitchen is because they want to consult a recipe. What if I told you that you don't need a recipe?

If you are brand new to cooking, or to cooking without animal products, of course I can understand that some guidance is welcome. Recipes are great for that! But here is a revolutionary approach to learning: carefully read the recipe you want to cook before you step into the kitchen. Pay attention to the list of ingredients and make note of where they appear in the instructions. Perhaps head to the kitchen, recipe in hand, and pull out the ingredients and tools you'll need. Seeing them there will serve as reminder of the steps you need to take. Visualize how you'll measure ingredients if needed, especially in cases where some require a teaspoon and others a tablespoon: it's a big difference. The good news is that if you make the mistake once, using one tablespoon of salt instead of one teaspoon, you'll have learned your lesson forever.

If you need a safety net, you can always jot some key steps and measurements on a piece of paper to jog your memory.

Once your mental setup is done, put your phone away, preferably in another room or under a couch cushion, and focus on cooking.

These initial steps will take you a "long" time the first few times you take them, and you may be slowed down by the extra caution you'll exercise when adding ingredients. However, it will not add an hour to your cooking time; more like ten minutes.

The upside is that you will be learning so much faster than if you just mindlessly followed the recipe, which in turn will enable you to cook faster – without recipes – in the near future.

If you are an intermediate plant-based cook with a few years of experience, I bet you know a lot more than you think about cooking. With a well-stocked fridge and pantry, and a few minutes to look at what you have and *think*, I'm certain that you can cook up a sizzling stir-fry, make a heart-warming chili or curry, or assemble a bowl with a luscious sauce. Notice I wrote "think," not "browse Pinterest."

There are delicious meal ideas within you! But they will only come out if you give yourself a chance to express them. If your mind is abuzz with the noise of all the beautiful dishes you could be making (as seen on Instagram), your own knowledge will never get into the spotlight.

Making something complex for the first time, say aquafaba macarons? Reading the recipe before you start is even more important! But you have my blessing to print it out. Better yet, transcribe it on a sheet of paper. The process of writing it down, preferably paraphrasing into your own shorthand lingo, will further embed the new knowledge into your brain and body. The result? You'll be more likely to (successfully) make macarons again. What's not to like?

What about cognitive offloading?

Smart devices are helpful when it comes to storing information that otherwise clutters our brains. Phone numbers, appointments, and lists of past presidents are safely stored in those mini encyclopedias we stuff in our pockets. Memorizing trivia is no longer needed! This is called cognitive offloading: delegating the task of remembering something to someone or something. It doesn't have to be a phone! Paper phone directories, commonplace books, and personal planners did the job quite well, but using connected devices instead offers genuinely practical new features.

Offloading facts to digital devices: I am all for it! But skills that we need on a thrice-daily basis? Not so much. And, yes, I consider the amount of spice to add to a chili to be a skill, not a fact: there is no right or wrong answer to "how much cumin should I add?" Clearly, "one cup" is too much, but you shouldn't need a recipe to tell you that after you have made chili even once – if you were paying attention. It is up to you to discover whether you like one teaspoon or two tablespoons.

There may be immediate benefits to offloading recipe keeping to your phone or tablet. However, as far as daily cooking is concerned, those benefits are insignificant compared to the negative side-effects. Far from making it faster to put dinner on the table, closely following recipes – and exposing yourself to the many distractions and temptations of your device – slows you down.

The limits of multi-tasking in the kitchen

Imagine this. You are preparing to enjoy your version of Every Mom's Bolo sauce on pasta tonight. You prepared the sauce during the weekend's batch cooking session (yay!), and it is now warming on the stove. You set a big pot of water on "high," and it is now boiling. You dump in the pasta, give it a stir, and set the timer on your phone for 10 minutes.

What do you do next? Set the table? Wash whatever dishes accumulated in the sink during the day? Or, since your phone is already in your hand, do you check your Instagram feed to give some "love" to @vegan.family.kitchen posts and reply to comments about your story?

Kitchens are the birthplace of multi-tasking. To successfully prepare meals on a short timeline, home cooks must remember to start cooking the rice before they heat up the skillet and chop their veggies. There are multiple tasks to juggle at once. We must constantly shift our attention from "watch those fingers!" to "is the water starting to boil?" to "I'm running out of balsamic vinegar." We use our eyes, ears, nose, taste buds, and skin to monitor the situation. For many of us, there are extra tasks, like preventing little children from running through the kitchen, greeting family members who are returning home (and listening to the stories they spontaneously start telling us), and repeatedly pushing back on requests for snacks because "dinner is going to be ready in just 5 minutes!"

No wonder we're looking to offload some of the cognitive action in our brains!

Instead of relying on mobile devices, I suggest offloading those recipes to a well-worn path in your nervous system by creating habits instead.

Because once the device is on the countertop – or even in our hand! – and the screen is on, we have added an extra layer of tasks that require mental energy. We must decide whether to act upon the many red notifications on our screens and the urge to check if something important (on email) or interesting (on social media) has come up in the last 12 minutes since we last checked. Every time we switch from the hot stove to our cool phone and back again, our brain needs time to get back to the task in front of it.

Let's give ourselves a break and stick to cooking.

Rest assured: nothing can really go wrong

When I cooked meat, I would always forget the safe core temperature for pork roasts, because I didn't make them often. That, I would agree, is information that can be offloaded — whether it is to an authoritative online source or to a piece of paper posted to the side of the refrigerator. Thankfully, I no longer need to know that.

One of the many benefits of cooking strictly plant-based foods is that very little can go completely wrong. In particular, food poisoning is a much less likely hazard. There are only three critical threats to your meal's edibility: excessive heat from appliances or from chili peppers, and excessive salt. Under-cooked tofu will not cause trichinosis or salmonella. In fact, you may discover it's delicious.

As you cook, you will encounter questions or problems. Asking Siri, Google, or Alexa for the solution is tempting. Resist! I challenge you to take note of the issue and think of a suitable solution all by yourself. I trust your intelligence and intuition. I know that you will come up with reasonable steps that will lead to an edible dinner. Notice the problem, remember the solution you came up with, and observe the results with curiosity. For particularly intriguing situations, you may even jot a handwritten note on a pad of paper to look something up on the Internet – or a book! – after your meal.

If the struggle defies your wits, consider calling your mom (if you are lucky enough to have her) or a friend with strong kitchen chops. It might save your dinner and enhance your relationship at the same time. Everyone loves feeling helpful.

Your phone and tablet are dirty

You already know this: mobile devices are dirtier than public toilet seats. We should be washing your hands before we start handling food, and again every time we use our devices while cooking. Isn't that absurd? Just put the phone away until after dinner.

Food porn is bad for you

What is food porn? It's that slick food styling and photography found in cookbooks but, more pervasively, on social media, especially Instagram. It's those appetizing blog images, the best of which are picked to feature on Pinterest.

Explicit videos are a poor substitute for sex education. In the same way, food porn makes a shaky foundation for cooking education. It creates unrealistic expectations about what weeknight family dinners should be like. The infinite variety of those images makes it harder for us home cooks to settle on one "good enough" dinner plan. Moreover, the sheer abundance of appealing imagery gives the impression that such culinary results can be reached effortlessly... whereas hours of preparation and multiple attempts were required to get the photos to look just right.

I encourage you to be critical consumers of food content. When you stumble upon a mouth-watering dish on a blog or social media, or in a cookbook, read the recipe carefully and tease out what makes it different from other similar dishes you have cooked in the past. Is it just the food styling and photography that make it look amazing, or is there something genuinely different about the ingredients and techniques used in the recipe? How can you apply what you just learned to your own cooking? Also read the comments to see whether others have tried cooking the dish and what they thought about it. Consume online food content (and cookbooks) mindfully. Then, take the lessons you learn into your kitchen – without your device!

Learn new cooking skills online, then go offline to put them to the test

In *Digital Minimalism*, Newport does not suggest that we should shut the Internet out of our life entirely, but rather that we should make intentional choices about how we use it. Digital media has made obscure knowledge and advanced skills accessible to all. The key is to know our purpose, carefully choose the content we will consume accordingly, and then disconnect to put our new skills to the test.

For example, I recently acquired a second-hand flat-bottom cast-iron wok. I spent about 30 minutes reading a few threads on specialized cooking forums about how to make the most of it, absorbing the experiences of others who were kind enough to share them with strangers on the Internet. I spent another 15 minutes watching a couple of videos about cast-iron wok cooking technique – which is a bit different from regular wok technique, because the thing is a solid 12 pounds, so not exactly something I can flick with my wrist to flip my tofu cubes over. Then – without my phone – I stepped into the kitchen. Wok cooking is all about high heat and speed: it would have been counter-productive to try to watch a video and cook at the same time. I needed to have all my attention in one place to avoid ruining dinner. (In case you wonder: the stir-fry was great!)

If you are interested in learning a new cooking technique, go ahead and read about it! Watch some highly rated, authoritative experts show you how in a video. Perhaps even sign up for an online course about it! While you are reading, read. While you are watching, watch. While you are taking the course, take notes and learn. Then, do.

Why we escape to social media

I am not immune to the call of my phone in the kitchen. What triggers me to pick it up while I am (supposed to be) cooking? Understanding what pulls us away from what is right in front of us, and what makes us so willing to let our attention be kidnapped, is key to changing our behavior in favor of greater presence and mindfulness.

I'll be brutally honest here. At 5 pm, I am tired and a bit hungry. My children are tired and very hungry. My husband is likely on his way home from work. He is also tired and hungry. As a work-from-home mom at the mercy of my kids' school calendar and unexpected tummy aches, there are times when I feel frustrated not to have been able to do all I wish I had done in the day. I admit to sometimes even being resentful about having to plan, prep, and cook dinner, and clean up, night after night for an audience that is often not grateful for my efforts – especially the little people.

What do I do? Between bouts of chopping, stirring, or cleaning, I seek connection with others who I think "get it." Maybe I connect with a remote friend by text message. Maybe I compulsively check whether my email subscribers have been reading the newsletter I sent a few hours ago. Maybe I scroll through my Facebook feed looking for questions I can answer in plant-based cooking groups. Instead of being where I am, I try to escape to a different part of my reality where I hope to feel more appreciated. But those interactions remain fleeting and not-so-satisfying.

What can I do instead? When I put away my phone and shut down my computer, I can be more present with the task at hand – cooking – and get it done faster. Sometimes, I manage to think of a little something I can do to make the meal more appealing to my kids, so they are more likely to eat it. While I wait for the broccoli to finish steaming, I can wash the lunch boxes, so that I will be able to step out of the kitchen sooner after dinner. Being present with the task of cooking now means that I can be more present with other aspects of my life later.

If you also have a habit of escaping to a world of remote connections through your phone, including while you are cooking, you may want to ask yourself why. Once you know, assess your success at fulfilling your needs that way. Did checking your phone really make you feel better? Now, you are better positioned to make decisions about whether that's a practice you want to continue or curb.

Practice now

I challenge you to cook screen-free for one week. Decide ahead of time where you will store your phone while you are cooking. Consider shutting down notifications or setting your phone into "airplane" mode. Plan your meals, pull out your ingredients and jot down notes if needed. Then, get cooking and keep cooking. Perhaps plan to keep the phone off until you are done eating and cleaning up, too.

While you are in the kitchen, there is a strong chance you will feel an urge to check something on your phone. Notice that urge. Take a breath. Tell yourself: "It's OK to want to check my phone. I will do it later." Take another breath. Let the urge go and keep on cooking.

CHAPTER 10

Keep the really good food flowing

Flow, by definition, means moving along steadily and continuously. In nature, gravity pulls water down rivers, from upstream lakes to the sea. Meanwhile, energy from the sun allows the H_2O molecules to become vapor, form clouds, and eventually return to the mountain tops to restart the cycle. In your kitchen, you are at once the sea and the sun. You are filled, nourished, and energized by the food you cook and eat, and you put some of that energy back into cooking up really good food.

Getting this symbiotic system started can be challenging if you don't already have a habit or culture of home cooking. Once the virtuous cycle has been initiated, keeping it flowing and carrying the momentum is critical. In this chapter, I will give you some tools to facilitate uninterrupted flow.

Beware: you will often be tempted to skip this or that step of your flow process because so many "more important" demands are made on your time. It happens to me, too. This chapters offers tools you can wield against such disruptions… and offers you a strategy to get back in the rhythm when, inevitably, at some point, you miss a beat.

Find your weekly routine

At different stages of life, different routines will work for you. You have to find your own, stick to it for a while, assess its results, and adjust it accordingly.

Currently, my children are aged 7 and 10, and my husband and I both work Monday to Friday in the daytime (though I work only during school hours). This is our current household routine:

- Friday before dinner: Before cooking, I actively reflect on the past week by looking at what's left in the fridge (left-over cooked dishes and fresh produce). I try to integrate what I find into that night's meal or plan to use them the next day. That will often lead to scrambled tofu with lots of veggies and a side of soup on Saturday for lunch.
- Friday after dinner: I glance at the past week's meal plan to remind myself which meals felt great (in terms of both process and results). My husband and I might talk about it as we clean up the kitchen. After the dishes are done, I soak some beans (usually chickpeas and black beans, but sometimes white beans, pintos, or others). Since I use my Vegan Meal Plans, I don't need to create

a meal plan from scratch, but if I did, I would create a quick rough draft at this time.

- Saturday morning: I go to the gym early then enjoy a lazy breakfast as the kids watch cartoons. At the same time, I look at the meal plan for the coming week and add items to my shopping list.

- Saturday mid-day: While the kids are at various activities, I shop for groceries. If the stars align, we might go to the farmers' market together for extra-nice veggies. The kids will want to buy some extra fruit and that's an impulsive purchase I am OK with. Back at home, putting away the groceries sometimes takes a while as I refill containers, organize the pantry, or clean the inside of the fridge.

- Sunday morning: It's meal prep time! After a long run, breakfast, and shower, I slap on an apron, crank up the tunes, and get cooking.

What routine might work for you?

Don't skip the reflection part!

Practicing flow in the kitchen requires paying increased attention to what exactly is happening in there. This is true in the moment, which is why I recommend leaving mobile devices outside the kitchen and off the dining table. It is also true in hindsight. Thinking back about my week, I ask myself:

- What am I grateful for when it comes to the past week's meals? I think back on the time and effort that went into growing, transporting, and selling the ingredients I made into dishes, the energy devoted to creating recipes, actually cooking the food, washing the dishes, taking out the trash, and my family's commitment to showing up together at the dinner table.

- What meals felt easy? Which ones felt like a struggle?
- For challenging meals, was the struggle in the cooking process or at the table?
- What did I handle successfully? What could have I done better?
- What meals or flavors received thumbs up from one or more person? What ended on the compost pile?

You can keep a running list of successful meal ideas and post it to your fridge for future reference.

Know what will interrupt your flow

I know that you agree with me that there are few things more important than feeding ourselves and our loved ones really good food that nourishes our bodies and souls. Yet, I bet you are just as likely as I am to sometimes drop the ball on it.

When there is a birthday party at the time when I'd normally get groceries, I tend to push grocery shopping to "later…" as if I was going to go to the store on a Saturday evening. Of course, I don't, so I have to shop for groceries Sunday morning, displacing my batch cooking session. After bringing home the groceries and performing all of the associated kitchen tasks, I need to step out of the kitchen for a break. The batch cooking doesn't get done, or it gets done begrudgingly.

When I travel, I tend to book my return trip for the Sunday right before we go back to work and school. Meals in the week that follows are bound to be a haphazard collection of previously frozen leftovers and pasta dishes with instant sauces (see appendix for instructions). Lunch boxes will be filled with less-than-wholesome foods. Nothing terrible, but not as satisfying as thoughtfully chosen and prepared meals.

When someone gets sick and misses a day or three of school, my work routine is disrupted, causing me to scramble to catch up during the weekend. Meal planning and batch cooking fall off the edge of my schedule.

I know what is likely to disrupt my cooking flow, and I bet you know what is likely to disrupt yours, too. Making a mental list of those, and seeing them coming, allows us to prevent the normal disruptions from ruining so many weeks' meals.

Preventing falls

Here are some actions we can take to prevent those normal, expected disruptions from ruining our dinners:

- When going away, do the meal planning and batch cooking for the week after you return beforehand.
- In the weeks before major disruptions or travel when you know your normal flow will be impossible, cook up double batches of your favorite hearty soups and stews (chilis, curries, etc.). Pack up the leftovers and freeze them so that that you have some simmered dishes to look forward to upon your return.
- Adjust your expectations (see chapter 2 about conscious compromise) and appreciate simpler meals for a few days.
- Take your cooking needs into consideration when booking travel. An extra day away isn't always worth it.
- Think about other, less important routines that you can

adjust or discontinue in order to save space for your cooking flow.

- Practice saying "no" to social events and commitments that aren't as rewarding as cooking really good food for yourself and your loved ones.
- Remind yourself of the value, enjoyment, and health you get from thoughtfully planning, cooking, and eating your meals.

What if there never is a good time to plan and prep?

We all get 168 hours every week, but we have varying degrees of control over how we use those hours. There are millions of people in North America alone who simply do not have the leisure to cook really good food for themselves. Many women and men juggle multiple demanding jobs, long commutes, and caregiving commitments. Some people's bandwidth is consumed by uncertainty or stress. If cooking is competing against napping when a couple of hours miraculously avail themselves, napping wins every time.

Meanwhile, as Neil Postman wrote in 1985 in reference to television, millions are amusing themselves to death.

Today, in addition to TV, we have Netflix, TikTok, and a plethora of social media sites grabbing our time and attention.

Endless, continuous, mindless entertainment is literally at our fingertips.

True, we can be so tired from our day job that choosing to plop ourselves on the couch to watch a favorite show feels like the right thing to do. I admit that video content creators can be very talented; many deserve the attention they garner. But we must recognize that entertainment for what it is: numbing cream for the soul as we ache from stressful, and sometimes meaningless, occupations.

At the risk of sounding dramatic, the consequence of choosing amusement over cooking really good food is indeed death. If we end up eating mostly prepared or processed foods made with copious amounts of added fat, sugar, and sodium, chronic disease will sicken us sooner rather than later.

It might be time to rebel.

What is the point of earning more money if our health pays the price?

Are our renovated homes, expensive vehicles, fancy mobile devices, and exotic travels worth sacrificing our physical and mental health?

If we continue with our busy work lives because we want to provide *more* for loved ones, let's zoom out and think about the true cost of our actions for a moment. Are our children benefiting more from private school or extracurriculars, or from nutritious meals and stress-free time spent with their families? Would children rather get a new electronic device now or enjoy a hike with their aging parent in 30 years?

We do not all have the freedom to design our lifestyle to pursue greater nourishment of the body and soul. But those of us who do have some wiggle room need the courage to make different choices.

Those choices might include a steadfast commitment to planning, preparing, and serving healthful meals.

Is that revolutionary or what?

When you fall off your plan and prep flow

Despite our best intentions and best laid plans, we do end up falling off the wagon. What next?

The first step is to *notice* what has happened.

Then, give ourselves grace for the interruption.

And now, get started again.

If this was a book about writing or another creative practice, or about fitness, I would nudge you to get into it for only five minutes. Write one sentence. Do two push-ups. Just sit down on a chair, close your eyes, and focus on your breath for a minute. See what happens next.

But if you haven't been cooking home-made meals for a few weeks, or even months, or years, you might have real physical obstacles in the way of engaging with your healthy vegan cooking flow. Start by chipping at those, in five-minute blitzes. You can:

- Wash some dishes.
- Open the fridge and take stock of your produce inventory. Toss rotting vegetables and wipe one shelf clean.
- Check your pantry and make a list of the whole foods you need to buy next time you hit the grocery store.
- Plan one simple meal for tomorrow and see if you can make it happen.

Then do it again.

Every meal is an opportunity

Many healthy habits get practiced every day. Whether you want to try meditation, write three pages in your journal, increase your volume of moderate exercise, or improve your bedtime routine, those are all things that tend to happen once per day.

The beauty of seeking flow in the kitchen is that we get three or more chances to practice every day. We get to feed ourselves and our loved ones breakfast, lunch, dinner, and snacks. In other words, we engage with food every few hours. There will be many obstacles, from time starvation to stress, and from budget woes to dietary restrictions.

Still, with a simple mindset shift, we can turn necessity into opportunity.

Let's practice flow in the kitchen.

Let's embark on a journey to instill gratitude, mindfulness, and love into the most fundamental gift we can offer: the gift of nourishing food.

PART TWO

UNDERSTANDING HEALTHY VEGAN COOKING

I invite you to join me in stepping away from the individual trees of single recipes to embrace the forest of healthy vegan cooking.

This section offers explanations about the structure and preparation of the basic building blocks of healthy vegan cooking.

Once you have read those instructions, you will start seeing everyday dishes differently. You will become empowered to improvise your own meals without relying on recipes.

My selection of building blocks covers some obvious basics (how to cook beans from scratch and whole grains) and some arbitrary choices (how to make soups and stews, stir-fries, salads and bowls, pizza, and sauces) that reflect my food culture and cooking style. Once you understand the approach, you will be able to apply it to the standards of your household's food culture.

You will never look at a recipe the same way.

COOKING WHOLE GRAINS

Cooking whole grains to perfection does not require looking up ratios, digging out measuring cups, or buying special appliances.

Some people call this method the "pasta" method. It works for brown and red rice, quinoa, farro, wheatberries, barley, and more. It does not apply to couscous (follow package directions) or risotto.

Here's the overview:

1. Pick a big pot.
2. Put a lot of water in it.
3. Bring it to a boil.
4. Meanwhile, rinse your grains using a fine-mesh metal strainer, until the water runs clear.
5. When the water boils, add the rinsed grains to the water. Stir well.
6. If inexperienced with that specific grain, set a timer for 10 minutes. If you know better, set a more precise timer.
7. Stir occasionally, making sure nothing sticks to the bottom.
8. When the timer goes off, taste a few grains. Are they still quite hard and gritty? Extend the timer by 2-3 minutes at a time and taste again until the grains are tooth-tender but not mushy.
   a. For quinoa that will be 12 to 15 minutes.

    b.   For brown rice, that will be 22 minutes.

    c.   For other grains, cooking time can vary more widely from one variety to the next. Taste often to prevent overcooking.

9. Stop the heat and carefully pour the cooking water through the fine-mesh metal strainer. Make sure most of the water has been removed, but no need to get rid of every last drop. It's more important to do this step quickly to preserve the heat.

10. Immediately return the cooked grains to the hot pot, cover with the lid, and set the pot on a trivet on the counter. The grains will finish steaming. Let it rest 10 to 15 minutes.

11. Uncover, fluff with a fork, and enjoy.

Cooking brown rice? Do not try other methods.

Aside from not having to remember the ratios corresponding to different kinds of rice, this method has another benefit: it reduces the amount of toxic arsenic found in rice.

If you haven't heard the news about arsenic in rice, no need to panic. Yes, brown rice grown in certain soils (notably those that used to grow cotton crops) contains more arsenic than is acceptable. Yes, arsenic consumption increases one's risk of lung and bladder cancer. But the risk must be put in perspective: according to FDA calculations, only about 39 cases of lung and bladder cancer per million people are attributable to arsenic exposure from rice. That's just a drop in the bucket of lung and bladder cancers.[4] Quitting smoking and bugging your elected representatives for regulations that limit air and water pollution might be more effective at decreasing your cancer risk than changing your rice cooking methods.

But if we can reduce our arsenic exposure with a simple tweak in our cooking routine, why not do it? After all, both lung and bladder cancers are quite awful, and I prefer to avoid hospitals. Since there is a method of cooking rice that is both safer and easier, why not adopt it and avoid unnecessary risk?

The toxic arsenic content of rice varies largely based on where it was grown. Some companies claim that their rice has been tested and does not contain notable amounts of arsenic. That is reassuring; however, I cannot seem to remember which origins and companies are "safe" and which aren't. Also, I mistrust food labels. Plus, I usually buy rice in bulk to reduce packaging waste, and the provenance of bulk rice is even harder to ascertain. Instead of relying on testing, I prefer to stick to this safer method to cook brown rice, which happens to be the simplest.

As described in a detailed review of recent studies by Dr. Michael Greger on nutritionfacts.org, rinsing and then cooking brown rice in a large volume of water as described above reduces the arsenic content to the point where they aren't significant health threats.

Unfortunately, this method also reduces the amount of iron and of some vitamins contained in the rice, including folate. If you are already eating a whole foods plant-based diet with

---

4   If you are curious about this issue, the FDA document "Arsenic in Rice and Rice Products Risk Assessment Report" is a must-read: https://www.fda.gov/media/96071/download.

lots of vegetables (including lots of greens and cruciferous veggies), you probably consume plenty of those vitamins already. I personally choose to have one extra piece of broccoli and not worry about it.

I should note that Dr. Greger himself no longer recommends eating brown rice since there are arsenic-free alternatives. For myself and my family, I determined that the risk is small enough (when cooked according to the method above) to continue eating brown rice in moderation.

What about using the Instant Pot?

Electric pressure cookers such as the Instant Pot are perfect for cooking beans from scratch (see next section). However, I do not recommend using them for whole grains, for two reasons.

First, most whole grains have a narrow margin of error when it comes to doneness. Cook them three minutes too little and they are hard as rocks. Cook them three minutes too much and they are mushy. Because it is not possible to lift the lid of electric pressure cookers to taste the grains for doneness until the pressure has been removed, cooking whole grains in the Instant Pot requires high confidence in your timing.

Second, one would need to know and follow grain-to-water ratios. Aside from the fact that I hate having to remember ratios, it is also not the preferable way for cooking brown rice.

Can anything replace the fine-mesh metal strainer?

I don't think so. Pasta strainers will let too many grains escape through the holes. Fine-mesh strainers made of plastic might warp when the boiling hot water is poured through, in addition to possibly contaminating your food with plastic residue. I consider a quality fine-mesh metal strainer an essential tool in a healthy vegan kitchen. If buying a new one, make sure you can use it hands-free, because you will need your two hands to lift the hot pot full of water and cooked grains. Mine has a long-enough handle that it can hang from the edges of my sink, like a bridge. Others have little legs so they can stand on their own safely on the bottom of your sink.

Freezing cooked whole grains

A downside of the "cook like pasta" method is that it takes a little longer than the conventional ratio-based method, since there is a bigger volume of water to boil. That's why I batch cook and freeze whole grains.

Three cups of whole grains fit comfortably in my fine-mesh metal strainer for rinsing and draining, so that's the quantity I make at a time.

Once the grains are done steaming and I have fluffed them with a fork, I uncover them to cool a little faster, then transfer to glass storage containers with airtight lids. Don't forget labels!

Using zip-top freezer bags is convenient and they can be reused multiple times since it's only grains; however, make sure to let your grains cool almost to room temperature before transferring to anything made of plastic. If storing in zip-top bags, lay them flat: the grains will thaw faster, and your freezer will look neater.

How to thaw the brown rice after freezing

If I think about it, I transfer the frozen rice to the fridge the night before, but usually I forget. I uncover the glass containers, sprinkle with a little water and thaw then heat in the microwave. The first few minutes, I use low power (60%) then a higher power to finish off. The whole process takes about 10 minutes and yields perfect brown rice, just as good as fresh.

If you do not have a microwave, reheating on the stove works great if your rice was previously thawed. Just transfer to a pot or skillet, use medium-low heat, and stir often.

Thawed rice is also perfect for fried-rice-style dishes.

What to do with cooked whole grains?

The possibilities are endless. You can eat it as-is in a bowl with roasted veggies, combine with beans to make falafel-like patties out of them, or serve them in a hearty salad. Of course, they can serve as a warm bed for stir-fries and simmered dishes like chilis and curries.

Whole grains can also be fabulous for breakfast. Quinoa or buckwheat are fabulous for breakfast porridge, for example.

COOKING DRY BEANS FROM SCRATCH

Everyone, vegan or not, should eat at least a cup of cooked beans every day. And what's the best way to stock your pantry with wholesome beans? In my opinion, nothing beats cooking dry beans from scratch.

In this section, I will:

- explain why I consider it better to cook dry beans from scratch,
- teach you the one method I use to cook all beans (which is very similar to the whole grain cooking method I showed you in the previous section),
- weigh in on some controversies (to soak or not to soak? to salt or not to salt?),
- provide detailed instructions for stovetop, electric pressure cooker (Instant Pot), and slow cooker bean cooking,
- and suggest the best way to store your beans once cooked.

And since no prose about beans is complete without a discussion of gas and farts, there'll be some of that sprinkled in, too.

Beans, peas, and lentils: what is this about?

To be clear: this section is about cooking dry beans and chickpeas from scratch, not about cooking lentils. Beans tend to be shaped like an oval or kidney, and larger. Peas like chickpeas tend to be spherical. Lentils are more like tiny discs, some of which have had their outer layer removed and/or have been split in half (like red lentils).

Botanically speaking, lentils are close to beans and peas, but they tend to behave differently when it comes to cooking, so I will not be discussing them here.

Why do I recommend cooking dry beans from scratch?

Canned beans are convenient and perfectly nutritious. There is absolutely no shame in using them.

Still, I prefer cooking dry beans from scratch. Here's why:

- They're cheaper (even when counting the cost of energy that goes into cooking them at home).
- They taste better, especially when fresh. Nothing beats a scoop of freshly cooked cannellini beans with a sprinkle of salt and a few drops of olive oil.
- There are many different varieties available, especially in ethnic food markets and via online order.
- They have less added salt (or none, if you don't add any while cooking).
- They take up less room in your cupboards.
- Dry beans are lighter to carry than canned beans, which makes it more manageable to get groceries on foot or by bike as opposed to driving.
- Dry beans can be bought in bulk (zero-waste). Even the packaged ones come in reasonably diminutive plastic bags. Comparatively, canned beans come in metal containers that take a great deal of energy to recycle

(including your effort carrying the blue bin to the curb or driving them to the recycling center).

- Food cans are often lined with plastic that might leach into your food at high heat during the canning process.
- It's just one more way to practice empowered cooking and take greater control and ownership of your food.

But is it OK to eat canned beans?

I prefer cooking my own dry beans from scratch, but I'd rather have canned beans than no beans. I keep a few cans at the back of my pantry just in case and more in my family's emergency kit.

The process of cooking dry beans from scratch isn't as involved as one might think. I think the total active time is only about 15 minutes (between preparing the beans by soaking, setting up the cooker, putting the cooked beans away, and washing the pot). But I can see how it might feel overwhelming and just "too much" for many people right now. I get it.

If that's you, come back to this section some other time. No worries!

One method to cook them all

Some beans cook quickly, others take their time. Making matters worse, the same type of beans from different batches – or even from a single bag! – can cook differently. One could study the matter in fine detail and write a book on the topic, but I prefer to use my "one method works for most" approach, as I do for cooking whole grains.

I am not a bean perfectionist. My priority is to avoid undercooked beans, which cannot always be saved once the initial cooking phase is completed. I am comfortable with slightly overcooked beans. On occasion, there might be more "blow outs" (broken outer skins on black beans) but that is a very distant consideration for me.

The most important thing for my family is to have fresh-cooked beans, and lots of them, without having to think too much about it. Accepting life with minor imperfections is what makes the practice of cooking daily meals at home from whole foods sustainable.

To soak or not to soak

I prefer to soak beans for 6 to 12 hours then rinse them with fresh water before cooking for a few reasons:

- It decreases cooking time, which makes the process more energy efficient.
- If cooking on the stovetop, it decreases the amount of moisture released in my home.
- It decreases the amount of phytates which, though they aren't bad for us, inhibit iron absorption.
- It increases nutrient availability as soaking triggers the early stages of sprouting.
- It possibly decreases gas.

Typically, I soak dry beans by putting about two cups in a big bowl on Friday night, so they are ready to cook Saturday morning. I usually make two different batches of beans every week, based on the ingredients of the current Vegan Meal Plan. Most of the beans will go in composed dishes, but we also eat some simply sprinkled on salads or on their own.

What happens if you cook dry beans without soaking?

Cooking dry beans without soaking takes longer and I find the results less consistent. I hate removing the lid of the Instant Pot only to find out that my beans are undercooked! Plus, the beans may be less nutritious that way.

If you wish to cook dry beans in an electric pressure cooker (Instant Pot) without soaking, you will need to at least double, and perhaps triple, the time.

On the stovetop, it will probably take an extra 20 to 40 minutes. See instructions below.

To salt or not to salt

Some food writers with a lot of time on their hands have extensively tested the impact of salting beans on cooked-bean outcomes. There are also tests involving baking soda.

Though there appears to be some benefits in terms of reduced cooking time, better color, and retained shape of the cooked beans in some experiments when adding sources of sodium to the cooking water (salt or baking soda), I do not personally recommend salting beans to cook them from scratch.

Despite the salt industry's efforts to seed controversy in the debate about the link between sodium consumption and disease, excess salt consumption remains the leading culprit of diet-related mortality. That's true for people with non-elevated blood pressure, too, despite everything you might have heard to the contrary.

In that context, adding a teaspoon of salt (almost 2,500 mg of sodium) to my beans is simply unnecessary.

When living in an over-salted world, the salt-free taste may take a little while to get used to. But it's still the right thing to do. After a few batches you won't be thinking about it anymore.

To season or not to season

I cook my beans from scratch as a substitute to canned beans, so I don't personally add seasonings when cooking them. Others like to throw some seasonings straight into the pot to add flavor to the beans. Here are some ideas:

- Asafetida (sometimes spelled asafoetida, and also called hing) is a very pungent seasoning most used in Indian food. Although it originates from the sap of a plant, it is usually found as a powder that will be either light yellow or white. It's used as a substitute for onion and garlic, which are not allowed in Brahmin and Jain cooking. Use just a pinch! Apparently, it also helps reduce flatulence induced by beans (see below), though I have not seen an actual study on the topic.

- Bouquet garni: this is a classic package of aromatic herbs such as parsley, thyme, and bay leaves. I have seen sage used often too. Tie the herb stems together (or put them in a little bag made of cheesecloth) and throw it in with the beans when cooking. Discard before draining.

- Add a carrot, an onion, or perhaps something like the green part of leeks to the cooking water. Discard before draining.

- Some vegetable broth powder or bouillon paste would add taste as well... just be aware that most have quite a bit of sodium.

- Thinking about adding salt? See section above.

Why do I add seaweed?

Kombu is a sea vegetable very high in iodine, so high in fact that you should not eat it straight up. I add a small amount (approximately 2 square inches) to the water when cooking light-colored beans like chickpeas or Great Northern, making sure to remove it before draining the beans. I don't add it when cooking black beans because I have a hard time discerning the kombu in the dark-colored cooking water, making it hard to discard all of it before draining.

If you regularly use iodized salt, there is no need to add kombu.

Stovetop, IP, or slow cooker: what is the best way?

My favorite method for cooking beans is in the Instant Pot, but there are other very valid approaches.

Stovetop method

1. Check your beans for rocks, just in case.
2. Soak the dry beans in plenty of water, 6 to 12 hours.
3. Drain and rinse the beans.
4. Place the beans in a big pot.
5. Add water to cover the beans by at least 3 inches (10 centimeters).
6. Add a piece of kombu, if using.
7. Cover with lid.
8. Bring the pot to a boil on high heat, then decrease the heat a bit to maintain an active simmer without overboiling.
9. From the 30-minute mark onward, test your beans by pulling one out with a slotted spoon every few minutes. Keep on cooking until they are pleasantly tender. Don't let them go mushy! (Actual time will vary between 30 and 90 minutes.)

10. When the beans are done, turn off the heat and either drain the beans through a metal strainer or transfer them to a glass jar or container using a ladle to keep some of the cooking liquid. If freezing, make sure to use straight-walled jars or containers and leave an inch of space at the top to avoid breakage.

11. Allow to cool before refrigerating or freezing.

Instant Pot (electric pressure cooker) method

Cooking dry beans from scratch is the top job of my Instant Pot. Even if that was the only thing it did, it would be enough to earn its keep in my kitchen.

1. Check your beans for rocks, just in case.
2. Soak the dry beans in plenty of water, 6 to 12 hours.
3. Drain and rinse the beans.
4. Place the beans in the metal insert of the electric pressure cooker.
5. Add water to cover the beans by about 1 inch / 2 centimeters.
6. Add a piece of kombu, if using.
7. Lock the lid on.
8. Cook on high pressure for the required time:
   a. Chickpeas: 14 minutes
   b. Black beans: 6 minutes
   c. Small white beans: 7 minutes
   d. Kidney beans: 8 minutes
   e. Other beans? Get the authoritative timing chart from Jill Nussinow – well worth the small investment for all the work she put into creating

that resource.[5] (I taped my chart inside my kitchen cabinet for quick reference.)

9. Allow pressure to release naturally for at least 15-20 minutes before releasing any residual pressure. Carefully open the lid.

10. Use a slotted spoon or tongs to remove kombu.

11. Either drain the beans or use a metal spoon to transfer them to glass jars or containers with some of their liquid. If freezing, make sure to use straight-walled jars and leave an inch of space at the top to prevent breakage.

12. Allow to cool before refrigerating or freezing.

Slow cooker method (and a warning)

Do not cook white, kidney, fava, black, or other kinds of oblong beans in the slow cooker. Though the risk is low, there is a chance you could make yourself very sick. Why?

Some kinds of raw beans contain a protein called phytohemagglutinin. (Latin root words: phyto means plant, hema means blood, and glutinin means protein that causes clumping up. English translation: not good.) Phytohemagglutinin is toxic to humans and needs to be broken down by cooking for enough time at a sufficiently high temperature. The greatest concentration of this protein is in kidney and white (cannellini) beans, but other beans – even black beans – have enough to cause issues for some.

If ingested by a healthy person, the "enemy" protein will be detected once in the stomach. Vomiting will follow, ejecting the

---

5　The Veggie Queen's "Best Vegan Pressure Cooker Timing Charts" are available here: https://www.theveggiequeen.com/product/best-vegan-pressure-cooker-timing-charts/

toxin from the body. However, some people's bodies may be compromised and not react strongly enough, leading to grave consequences. Why take a chance?

Slow cookers are basic appliances and unfortunately do not reach a sufficiently high temperature, or do not stay there for a long-enough time to guarantee that the toxin will be destroyed. The other cooking methods described here (stovetop and electric pressure cooker) are more suitable for cooking those types of beans, and perfectly safe.

The only bean I suggest cooking in the slow cooker is chickpeas (which has no phytohemagglutinin). It is in fact my preferred method to generate aquafaba (the "water of beans" that can be used to make delightfully airy chocolate mousse). Rinse 2 cups of chickpeas (no soaking necessary), add to your slow cooker with 5 ½ cups of water and a 2-inch piece of kombu. Cook on low for 9 hours. Discard the kombu and strain the chickpeas out, keeping the aquafaba for your other purposes. (Freeze it in an ice cube mold for convenience.)

Lentils are also fine to cook in the slow cooker.

Help! My beans didn't soften

If you cook your beans for hours and they never soften, they might just be old. Try to buy beans from a store that moves a lot of them, so they are fresher. Don't stockpile more beans than you can cook in the next few months.

Storing your cooked beans

Cooked beans must be refrigerated (they will keep for 5 days, perhaps more if kept sealed) or frozen.

Here are two good ways to store your cooked beans:

- Straight-walled, wide-mouth mason jars are my favorites. The 2-cup / 500 mL size is perfect for beans because it's comparable to the amount from a can. If freezing, make sure to leave lots of space at the top for expansion (1 inch / 2 cm). Jars with "curved" shoulders may break in the freezer under the stress of expansion.
- Zip-top bags are a decent option, but you will need to allow the beans to cool down completely before transferring them. Label the bags carefully and lay them flat if freezing - the beans will thaw faster when you need them.

Eat those beans!

Plan to use some of your freshly cooked beans right after cooking them! It's the cook's treat. They have the perfect texture and taste. If I don't have an immediate plan for a meal, I'll have a scoop of drained beans with a sprinkle of salt (literally just a few crystals) and a few drops of olive oil. Amazing snack! Mixing in a handful of peppery arugula makes it heavenly. The greens will immediately wilt when mixed in with the hot beans.

What about gas?

The experience of gas and flatulence seems to be highly subjective. What seems to be windstorm to some may be just a casual breeze for others. I suspect that our respective culinary and cultural upbringings have a lot more to do with it than actual biochemical reactions to eating beans.

Most of the population consumes far too little fiber, and likely doesn't have the kind of gut microbiome that's used to digesting legumes. Omnivores may thus feel more bloating and gas after having a big bowl of rustic bean soup.

If one is experiencing painful bloating, a more careful and

progressive approach to increasing one's bean consumption is warranted. Start with a sprinkle of a few beans on top of your salad before progressively increasing your consumption to the desired 1 ½ cups daily.

If it's only the awkwardness of passing gas that bothers you, it may be time to search Google for "how to fart quietly." (I can't believe I am writing this, but someone's got to do it.)

Soaking the dry beans before cooking supposedly increases their digestibility by starting to break down the beans' sugars, therefore decreasing gas. In practice, I am not absolutely certain that it makes a difference.

Asafetida (hing) and bay leaves are thought by some to decrease flatulence from bean consumption, but I haven't found a science-backed source for this assertion.

Finally, I don't want to say that vegans' farts don't smell bad… but if there is no rotting animal flesh in one's bowels, the smell of passing gas is far less offensive. At least, that is what I have observed when my husband transitioned to a 100% plant-based diet. (The noise still annoys me, but the smell is mostly gone.) Stop eating animals and see what happens.

Whatever it takes, just eat those beans

Your future health partially hinges on increasing your bean consumption to 1 to 2 cups per day. As Dr. Greger says, "just stick with it." Choose the cooking method and approach that best suits your needs and schedule, and if needed just get canned beans and call it a day.

Soups and Stews

Soup is part of the solution to every problem worth solving in the world: hunger, of course, but also sickness, loneliness, anxiety, conflict, income inequality, fiber and vitamin deficiencies, and animal agriculture (among others). And the best thing about it is that even absolute beginners can learn how to make vegan soup and get a decent bowl of plant-based goodness on the table in minutes.

Stews are just soup with less liquid.

(Stoups are somewhere in between.)

In this section, I will teach you how to make vegan soup and stews. At the time of publishing this, a Google search for the phrase "vegan soup recipe" returns an astonishing 204,000,000 results… which is ironic because the best soups are those you'll make without a recipe.

By best, I do mean tasty, but also nutritious, economical, satisfying, practical, and warm, too.

There are some basic principles that apply to every type of plant-based soup and stew you can possibly want to make. I will teach you those here. I will also explain how to make vegan soup or stew using your favorite kitchen appliances. But first, why make soups and stews?

Twelve reasons to cook soups and stews

- Soups and stews easily transport all the veggies into your tummy.
- It's a great way to use leftover or imperfect produce (raw or previously cooked).
- Soup and stews are perfect to integrate more greens and cruciferous veggies in your diet as well as healthful spices and herbs.
- Soups and stews are easy to make even for absolute vegan cooking beginners.
- Adding whole grains and legumes to your veggie soup or stew makes a complete meal in a single pot. Fewer dishes!
- You can set it and forget it (see slow cooker and Instant Pot methods below).
- All the nutrients stay in the cooking liquid, and some (like carrots) even release their nutrients better when cooked.
- Soups and stews are perfect for lunches: easy to reheat in the microwave or carry in a pre-heated Thermos.
- They freeze and thaw without a hitch.
- You can even dehydrate them for camping or for your emergency preparedness kit.
- It makes your home smell good, and your heart feel warm.
- Soups and stews are easy to share with others hungry souls.

Two soups or stews a week, that's the minimum!

Soup 1: Every meal prep session should include a soup or stew. It's quick and easy to make a big pot of your favorite and eat it throughout the week as an appetizer or side to other meals, or on its own. Make soup or stew every Sunday, refrigerate the fruit of your labor, and you'll never be without anything to eat during the week.

Soup 2: Even better, add a soup or stew to your weekday dinner plan. I include one in every week of my Vegan Meal Plans. Soups usually get served with a hearty side salad or grilled sandwiches, while stews stand on their own or atop some cooked grains. For convenience, I often suggest that the soups and stews be made in the slow cooker, because it allows to do the chopping at one time and the eating at another. Coming home to the aromas of a simmering dinner is a great weeknight boon!

Understanding the types of soup

Soup can be served with visible pieces of their components (barley and seitan soup) or look like a smooth, creamy, and homogeneous mixture (bisque of roasted red pepper) ... or a mix of both (cream of mushroom). Stews tend to be chunky.

Looking for something smooth? Traditionally, many soups are thickened by using either a starch (like flour or cornstarch) or heavy dairy cream. Although "vegan cream" is commercially available, I personally see no point in either of those techniques because they contribute little to no nutritional benefits, while adding refined and/or fatty ingredients. I prefer to simply blend my soup to the desired consistency using a hand-held "stick" blender or by carefully transferring it into my high-power blender (Vitamix) for extra-smooth results. If the soup is too thin, then next time I'll know to add more lentils, vegetables, or grains, or less liquid. If the soup is too thick, it's never too late to add hot vegetable broth.

Although I am certainly grateful for China's invention of paper, my favorite Asian cultural import is by far the noodle soup as a main dish. My life was transformed when I discovered Vietnamese phở in my teenage years and real Japanese ramen —

not the dehydrated stuff in plastic packages! – in my thirties. I still don't know why they feel so satisfying. It might have to do with the pleasure of a diversity of mouthfeels thanks to the different components in the soup, combined in a single bowl, along with the whole-body warmth imparted by the fragrant broth.

General soup and stew strategy

Always start by sautéing a diced onion, add a few extra vegetables, make sure there are seasonings like garlic, spices, and herbs, then add broth, and beans. More broth leads to a soup. Less broth leads to a stew.

You can also use canned tomatoes to make it more into a chili (great on roasted sweet potatoes, rice, tortillas, and more) or a rich tomato sauce like my versatile vegan bolo sauce (served on pasta, Portobello mushrooms, potatoes, or polenta).

Make your soup or stew into a complete meal by adding some grains, or plan on pairing it with whatever grain you cook for the week. Brown rice or whole wheat orzo noodles work well in soups. Quinoa melds nicely into a stew such as bean chili.

When all ingredients are cooked to tender, add a big handful of chopped greens (for even more nutrition) and stir them in. They'll wilt while the pot cools down a bit.

Standard stovetop approach

Do you really need a fat to start? I think not, but if you are just getting started on a plant-based diet, you might want to use a teaspoon of olive oil or two as it will enhance all flavors. If going oil-free but worried about sticking, have a little broth at the ready and add a tablespoon of it at a time when things get too dry.

Almost every dish benefits from getting a flavor jumpstart with the classic trio of onion, carrot, and celery (a.k.a. *mirepoix* in French and *soffrito* in Italian). Choose a good red onion (the red color indicates extra phytonutrients), dice it, and cook it with a big pinch of salt for at least 5 minutes while you chop the carrots and celery. Then, add those and let them cook for another 5-10 minutes while you get the remaining ingredients ready.

Use all parts of dark leafy greens by detaching the leaves from the stems and chopping the latter finely, adding them at the same time as the celery. The leaves should go in at the end, as they will wilt quickly and retain the most nutrients.

Denser vegetables and those cut into bigger chunks will take longer to cook, so add them right after the mirepoix. As the vegetables cook, their water content evaporates, and flavors become more concentrated.

It's not conventional, but I prefer to add garlic and ginger along with the spices, after the vegetables have cooked for a while. I find that it reduces the risk of burning them, especially since I use little to no oil. I add them to the pot and stir for a minute to ensure that they touch the hot surface. After 30 seconds to 2 minutes, when I can smell them, I deglaze.

Always deglaze. That means adding a small quantity (2 tablespoons to ½ cup) of cold liquid to your pot and letting it sizzle, energetically scraping the bottom with a flat wooden spatula at the same time to detach caramelized bits. Those are the sugars from the vegetables that you cooked, and they belong in your tummy, not at the bottom of the dirty dish water. (Bonus: deglazing also makes dishwashing quicker.) Great deglazing liquids include citrus juices, flavorful vinegars, wine, and vegetable broth. Water will do in a pinch.

Pro tip: Have your deglazing liquid ready before you add the garlic and spices.

After deglazing, add the hot vegetable broth. I find it easier to use a quality broth powder, which I throw straight into the pot, and pour in boiling water from the kettle. You could always use cold water but then you'll have to bring the pot back to a boil before simmering. If using canned tomatoes or coconut milk, now's the best time to add them as well.

If you are making soup, you are probably adding 5 to 6 cups of liquid in total.

If you are making stew, you are probably not adding more than 3 or 5 cups of liquid. (Canned tomatoes count as liquid in this calculation.)

Add other ingredients like beans, lentils, and/or grains (barley, rice, quinoa, amaranth, etc.). Stir well to make sure there are no clumps.

Do not add noodles now, however. They must go be added at the end, cooked separately.

Simmer the soup or stew for 20 minutes or until all ingredients are done to your liking. If you used ingredients like pot barley, you will need to simmer for longer. Taste to check.

Add dark leafy green leaves as well as fresh herbs, if using, and maybe another squirt of lemon juice depending on the soup's flavor profile.

Taste and adjust seasoning. Keep in mind that ready-made broth is often salty, so you probably need less salt than you think.

If making soup, blend if desired. Some stews are nice to blend a bit, too, but leave some chunks for a more diverse experience with every bite.

Don't forget the garnish! A little finishing touch (fresh herbs, a few pumpkin seeds, a sprinkle of chopped nuts, or a spiral of nutty cream) will elevate your soup. Croutons cut out of a piece of toast add some crunch. A squirt of lime works well, too.

Help yourself to a bowl while the soup cools enough to transfer to containers and refrigerate or freeze. (Don't forget to label it!)

What about noodle soups?

When making noodle soup, remember to cook the noodles separately, then drain and rinse with cold water to stop them from cooking into mush. Some, like rice noodles, just need to steep in super-hot water for a few minutes. To serve, place a handful of noodles in your bowl and ladle the hot soup on top. The noodles will warm up instantly.

To blend or not to blend? Just mix things up.

Some soups' cultural baggage makes us want to blend them smooth (Vichyssoise), others scream for chunks (minestrone). But rest assured, the soup police won't burst into your kitchen if you depart from tradition.

Don't think of blending as the secret weapon. Some picky eaters (children and adult alike) will prefer their soup blended smooth, which is a good opportunity for the cunning cook to sneak in extra nutrition. For example, red lentils completely break down during cooking and practically vanish when blending. Other selective eaters, however, are suspicious of mixtures when they cannot readily identify all ingredients.

A possible benefit of chunky soups is that they lead you to feel satisfied sooner and full for longer. I wouldn't say that there is a broad scientific consensus, as only a few studies have been done on the topic, but it does make sense that having something to chew keeps you on task for longer, giving your brain more time to get the stomach's message: "Hey, I'm full now. Stop telling the hand to lift the spoon!" In addition, chunks require more effort to digest than a homogeneous pulverized liquid. On the flip side, blended soups may have more readily absorbable nutrients.

If you're having two soups per week, just make one smooth and one chunky to hedge your bets.

Noodle soup should never, ever be blended – that would be a sacrilege! Unless, naturally, the recipient must eat it through a straw, in which case you might be better off using a whole grain anyway, such as quinoa, barley, millet, or amaranth, instead of a flour-based noodle.

Time-saving tip: If you plan on blending the soup, you can be sloppier with the chopping. Your vegetable chunks should still be roughly similar in size, but since everything will be blended smooth, no-one will notice that your garlic wasn't perfectly minced. Just slice it.

The stoup variation

For bring-along lunches, I often prefer "stoup" to soup. That's my made-up word for a dish that's halfway between a soup and a stew. It's great to serve on top of cooked rice or scoop with a piece of bread. If you have a big appetite but only a small container, stoup also packs more calories per volume.

To achieve stoup, you can either reduce the amount of broth or other liquids you put in or simmer the soup for longer (so more water evaporates, concentrating the flavors).

Many soups will accidentally become stoups as they cool and thicken. To return them to soup, you may need to stir in a little broth or hot water.

Slow cooker variation

The easiest way to make vegan soup or stew in the slow cooker is simply to put in all the ingredients into the crock and cook on low for 6-8 hours.

The downside is that slow cooking does not develop flavors in quite the same way as cooking on the stovetop, because the temperature that's safe to maintain while you're not looking (less than 200 degrees Fahrenheit) is lower than the temperature required for caramelization (around 300 degrees). To make up for this, you may feel the need to increase the amount of flavorings such as spices in your dish.

Slow cooking also requires less liquid (broth), because there is a lid on the crock, preventing evaporation. Using approximately 20% less liquid than you would for a stovetop recipe should do.

Instant Pot variation

The benefit of using an Instant Pot is that you can start cooking your vegetables on "sauté" mode, developing flavors as you would on the stovetop. You then hit "cancel," add the rest of the ingredients, and proceed to automatic high-pressure cooking. You'll want to set the timer based on the slowest-cooking ingredient.

Pressure cooking is not particularly faster than cooking on the stovetop, but if you are using an electric pressure cooker such as an Instant Pot, you can set it and forget it, as you would with a slow cooker.

Because pressure cooking is also done under cover, you will want to reduce the amount of liquid in your Instant Pot soup as well.

Soups and stews in the oven: why not?

If you have a full meal prep session on the go, different dishes may be competing for your stove's burners. Get the soup or stew started on the stovetop in an oven-safe pot with lid, deglaze, add the rest of the ingredients, then cover with an oven-safe lid and transfer to the oven at 300 degrees Fahrenheit (150 Celsius, gas mark 2). Simmer for about an hour.

Alternatively, you could put all ingredients in an oven-safe dish such as a Dutch oven, cover, and "bake" for two to three hours in the oven. This only makes sense from an energy standpoint if you already have other things in the oven. If you use this method, remember to carefully pull the soup out and stir it every hour or so.

An alternative approach is to chop the vegetables into big chunks, add to a Dutch oven, and toss with just a little olive oil. Roast at 375 degrees Fahrenheit (190 Celsius, gas mark 5) without the lid for 30-45 minutes, stirring once partway through. Then, bring the pot to the stovetop, add liquid ingredients, flavorings, and perhaps some beans, and simmer 20 minutes. Blend smooth and enjoy the sweet, caramelized flavors! Perfect if your oven is already on for something else.

Make soup with your power blender

High-power blenders' blades spin so fast that they generate enough heat to cook your soup. Those who aren't too bothered by loud noises can make a small batch of soup by adding a few vegetables, a handful of cooked beans, some liquid, and flavorings in the blender, gradually turning it on to high speed, and letting it spin for five minutes or until steaming. Don't overfill the blender and proceed with caution as it'll get quite hot. Few things ruin the day quite like beet soup that splashes all over your kitchen cabinets and ceiling.

STIR-FRIES

When it comes to improvising a meal from seasonal produce and pantry ingredients, creating a stir-fry might be the quickest path to dinner... but it requires some forethought.

The dry heat of the skillet – as opposed to the moist heat of a soup pot – means smaller margins of error. Leave a soup to simmer for too long and you might find yourself with mushy vegetables. Leave a stir-fry's vegetables in the skillet for too long and you might burn your dinner. Understanding the basic method for stir-frying a healthy vegan dinner will save you from having to refer to a recipe when seconds matter.

The essence of a stir-fry

Stir-fries have two characteristics that distinguish them from other dishes.

First, the heat is on. Your skillet will be heated on medium or higher. When ingredients hit the hot surface, their outer layer will caramelize and "seal" them, so they keep their distinct personality relative to the other ingredients. The heat must stay up throughout, so avoid adding lots of cold ingredients in at once. That would bring the temperature down and release too much water at once, leading to steaming rather than frying.

Second, time is of the essence. Once the first ingredients hit the hot skillet, there is no pause. The dish must come together quickly. It is essential to have the ingredients already prepared before starting. For home cooking, I am generally not a proponent of "mise en place" (advance measuring and/or chopping of all ingredients, neatly separated in prep bowls). However, to prevent lulls during which your food might burn or lose its optimal texture, stir-fries do require having everything at hand, ready to throw into the frying pan.

Components of a good weeknight stir-fry

What goes in a simple stir-fry to make it both tasty and nutritious, without taking a long time to prepare? There are five components:

- A super simple flavor profile. Advance prep would allow you to prepare a complex sauce, but combining just basic ingredients like garlic, ginger, lime, and soy sauce is enough.
- Vegetables make up about half of the dish. Start with an onion and add two, at most three other vegetables.
- Protein-dense foods make up a quarter.
- A starchy base fills the remaining quarter of your dish.
- Optional: add garnishes that enhance the dish without effort.

Equipment required to stir-fry

Stir-frying does not require special equipment. All you need is:

- A pot to prepare the starchy base (grain or noodles)
- A wok or large skillet to cook the vegetables and protein
- A wooden spatula
- A knife
- A large cutting board

If you also have prep bowls, it's great! (No need to buy

anything special, any regular bowl will do.) But keep in mind that you'll end up with more dishes to wash if you use them. I prefer using my largest cutting board and keeping the chopped vegetables on it until time to add them to the wok.

If you have a blender, it broadens the range of sauces you can prepare. (See "flavor boosters" below.)

Setting up your basic stir-fry components

First, choose your **vegetables**. I recommend always starting with an onion for great flavor and health benefits. Then, pick at least one cruciferous vegetable (broccoli, cauliflower, red cabbage, bok choi, gai lan…). Finally, add one, at most two extra vegetables of different colors. Bell peppers (red or orange are my favorites), carrots, zucchini, green beans, eggplant, and mushrooms are fantastic.

The onion should be diced small, whereas the other vegetables should be cut into pieces roughly as big as the end of your thumb… unless they are very dense vegetables (carrots, broccoli stems…) which should be sliced on the thinner size to cook quickly enough.

You can add a little fruit to your stir-fry. Peel a mandarin orange and divide it into pieces or dice a chunk of pineapple. In season, persimmon pieces are a fun add-in, too!

For **protein**, my favorite choice is firm or extra-firm tofu (calcium-set), but it is not the only option. Tempeh is also a classic. If you have some in the fridge already, seitan (vegan meat made from gluten) is also a great choice. Edamame pods work too. Though not something I recommend doing every day, some vegan meats from the store work great in stir-fries. In a pinch, any bean will do.

Tofu and beans must be patted dry to remove excess water for best results. I personally do not press tofu, though I cut it into slabs and pat each piece dry with a clean tea towel before cutting.

If using tofu, tempeh, or seitan, simply cut into dice, each about the size of the tip of your thumb.

Now, for the **starchy base**, I recommend using either cooked grains (see section on Cooking whole grains) that you already have in the fridge or noodles that can cook in less than 5 minutes. I love brown rice and soba noodles the best, but your options are endless. Spaghetti is a perfectly fine choice, too! As part of the set up, you should reheat the grains or cook the noodles (follow package directions). If using noodles, rinse them quickly with cold water once they are done cooking to stop them from turning too soft.

Finally, make sure that your **bonus ingredients** are also ready. Peanuts, cashew nuts, and sesame seeds add crunch. You will need roughly a tablespoon per serving. A few chopped leaves of cilantro create yet another flavor contrast. A forkful of vegan kimchi brings a pleasantly sour crunchy surprise. The kimchi can be set on the table for diners to help themselves.

Line up your flavor boosters

Garlic and ginger, both minced, add essential flavor and zing to any stir-fry. Make sure to prepare those before you start cooking and set aside.

Liquid seasonings bring it all together. I love a combination of soy sauce and little rice vinegar. Fruit juices (lime, lemon, orange, pineapple...) bring sweetness without refined sugar, but sometimes I use a teaspoon of maple syrup. A dash of hot sauce works, too. Experiment to find your favorite combo! Add a little at a time, taste, adjust, taste again, and repeat until you are satisfied with the results. When you eat the dish, notice what you like about it and make a mental note for next time if you think anything should be adjusted.

You can mix a little nut butter (peanut butter, pumpkin seed butter, tahini...) into the sauce, too.

If you have a blender with a small container, you can throw all the flavorings in the jar and blend until smooth. I love to blend two or three cloves of garlic, a thumb-sized piece of ginger (chopped into a few smaller pieces), two or three tablespoons of soy sauce, one or two tablespoons of lime juice (or half a peeled lime, seeds removed), a handful of peanuts or pistachios, and a teaspoon of maple syrup. You might need to add a little water to help the blades reach every bit. For a slightly decadent, saucy dish, add half a can of coconut milk.

If you are short on time or facing a bare pantry, a splash of soy sauce is good enough. When cooking at the cabin, I just use individual packets!

If you have a sure hand, you can simply have your liquid seasoning bottles at the ready. Splash in a tablespoon or two when the time comes. Alternatively, pre-mix them in a small bowl.

What about oil?

If we're frying, do we need oil?

Not *really*... but a little goes a long way to increase flavor and texture when cooking with high dry heat.

If you choose to use oil, choose one with a high smoke point, like canola, peanut, or avocado oil.

If cooking without oil, have some water at hand to add to

the work to prevent your food from sticking, a tablespoon or two at a time. That means you will be cooking with moist heat more than dry heat, hence the slightly different results, but the process remains similar.

Cook it all up

Now that you know what you are going to cook, it's time to bring it all together. Here are the general steps to follow to pull together a quick weeknight stir-fry.

1. Reheat your grains or prepare to cook your noodles according to package directions. You will have to monitor that process at the same time as you do the following steps.

2. Pull out your wok or skillet. If using cast-iron cookware, make sure to pre-heat for at least 10 to 15 minutes. You can start warming them on medium heat while you prepare the rest of the ingredients. Thin cookware (stainless steel, nonstick, etc.) should not be pre-heated for more than two or three minutes.

3. Dice your vegetables and lay them in piles on your cutting board. You can move them to prep bowls if your cutting board is too small.

4. Mince your garlic and ginger.

5. Line up your liquid seasonings or mix up a simple sauce.

6. Prepare your bonus ingredients and make sure the table is set. Have your plates or shallow bowls ready for serving.

7. Time to cook! If using tofu, tempeh, seitan, or vegan meat, start there. You'll want to cook the dice about five minutes, until golden on most sides. Transfer the protein to a bowl.

8. Add the onion to the wok with a pinch of salt. The salt will break down the cell walls of the onion, helping it sweat out its water content and concentrating the flavors. Cook for 1 minute, stirring every 20 seconds or so.

9. Add your densest vegetable and maybe another little pinch of salt. Cook for two or three minutes, stirring every minute or so.

10. Add the next vegetable, and cook for another two or three minutes, stirring occasionally. If using fruit, add last and move on to the next step immediately.

11. Push the vegetables together to expose some of your skillet's hot surface. If you are OK with oil, add just a teaspoon and throw the garlic and ginger in it. Stir for 30 seconds or until fragrant, then mix it all together with the vegetables.

12. Put the protein back into the wok.

13. Add the liquid seasonings.

14. Stir and give it all a chance to warm up for two minutes, stirring occasionally.

15. For beginners, I recommend simply putting the cooked grains or noodles at the bottom of each serving plate or bowl. Top with the stir-fried vegetables and protein foods. Once you feel more confident, and if your wok is big enough, you can practice mixing in your grains or noodles before serving.

16. Add toppings on each individual portion and serve.

SALADS AND BOWLS

Fresh produce year-round is not a bounty I take for granted. Maybe it's showing my age but, growing up, a "salad" in the winter meant a few chunks of iceberg lettuce with, maybe, slices of cucumber and halved cherry tomatoes. Today's global food distribution system brings the complete rainbow of fruit and vegetables, along with a broad selection of nuts, seeds, grains, and legumes, all of which can be enjoyed even during the darkest days of winter. Think of all the tasty morsels and healthful phytonutrients we can now enjoy! An awesome way to honor these colorful gems is to create satisfying vegan salads and bowls.

This section is where you learn to choose the right ingredients to make your salad into a complete, satiating main dish. As for any improvised meal, the key is to combine your favorite vegetables with protein rich foods and whole grains, then add flavorful touches and nutrition boosters. Keep these proportions in mind: half of your plate should be vegetables, a quarter whole grains, and a quarter protein-dense food.

A selection of bonus ingredients such as nuts, seeds, fruit, and spices will give your satisfying vegan salads their own unique personality and keep you coming back for delicious, nutritious seconds.

Hearty, satisfying vegan salads and bowls are also perfect for vegans to bring as a contribution to potlucks. Make your dish festive and tasty: not only it will open the minds of other guests to the beauty of vegan cooking, but it will provide you with a safe go-to you can pile high onto your plate.

Salad or bowl?

Salads tend to have their ingredients mixed together.

Bowls tend to have their main components side by side, though some can form a base layer while others are sprinkled evenly on top.

Salads can travel in a single, large bowl to serve a crowd.

Bowls are more of a personal thing.

Salads and bowls have similar components, so you can apply the same reasoning when improvising both.

Components for a satisfying vegan salad or bowl

Dark leafy greens: It wouldn't be a salad without the greens, would it? Romaine lettuce, watercress, kale, bok choy, spinach, they're all good! (Well, except perhaps iceberg lettuce which is just water in the shape of leaves.) Make sure your greens are clean and chop them in bite-size pieces. Other leafy veggies to consider (albeit perhaps not in the lead role) include radicchio and endives, in small amounts (until you get used to the bitterness).

Whole grain: My favorites for salads are quinoa, farro, and pearl barley, but brown rice, millet, and amaranth make great bases, too. Short pasta like orzo is an option as well. Couscous, also mechanically processed, is a time-saving favorite because it takes only 5 minutes to prepare – even in its whole wheat version.

Beans/protein-dense food: Chickpeas and black beans are my family's legumes of choice. But the sky is the limit when it comes to beanstalks, right? For salads and bowls, I tend to choose a bean based on color-coordination with the salad's other components. Edamame, which you can buy frozen without the shell, is another protein-rich choice. Personally, I am not a fan of lentils in salad, except French "de Puy" green lentils and black beluga lentils, which are firmer and more defined. Regardless of your chosen bean, it'll have to be cooked – unless you are lucky enough to have access to fresh summer peas. Canned is perfectly fine to use, but make sure to drain and rinse well. Tofu cubes can also stand in for legumes. I love dicing and sautéing firm tofu with salt and pepper for just 5 minutes, until golden on all sides. If I'm lucky enough to find smoked tofu, it's going in as-is, without cooking. Delicious!

Other vegetables: Think crunchy, colorful, and seasonal. On the raw side, I recommend diced red, orange, or yellow bell peppers, grated carrots, beets, or orange sweet potato, diced zucchini or cucumber, cherry tomatoes, small cauliflower or broccoli florets, green beans (cut into short pieces), and corn. All of those (except the cucumber) are delicious if roasted. Pair them on the baking sheet with mushrooms, eggplant, winter squash, and other root vegetables.

Nuts and seeds: Just a tablespoon of nuts or seeds makes a big difference in your salad experience by adding a pleasant texture diversion: crunch! Sprinkled on top or tossed in, almonds, hemp seeds, pine nuts, pumpkin seeds, sunflower seeds, cashews, sesame seeds, and walnuts bring a small amount of health-promoting plant-based fats, including in some cases precious omega-3s, as well as a variety of amino acids (protein) and nutrients, notably calcium and iron. Just a tablespoon per serving will elevate your dish to become a truly satisfying vegan salad.

Fruit: Many salad dressings include a sweetener… but why settle for a refined sugar when you can get that sweet hit straight from the fruit? Adding pieces of fruit to your satisfying vegan salad will create bursts of juicy sweetness and make your dish memorable. Fresh fruit like berries, halved grapes, pieces of mandarin orange, diced stone fruit (apricot, nectarines, peaches…), figs, or mango when they are in season, and even a simple diced apple work wonders. No fresh fruit? No problem! Always keep dried fruit in the pantry. My favorites are currants and raisins. Cranberries can be nice but are often sweetened. Dried and diced figs and apricots, if they aren't too hard, are also great.

Fresh herbs: Just like fruit, fresh herbs aren't absolutely required, but they'll boost the nutritional profile and flavor of your vegan salad. Chopped cilantro and parsley are fabulous. Basil has a lovely flavor, too – just cut into ribbons but don't overhandle, as the delicate leaves bruise easily.

Dressing: You need a liquid to tie it all together! The next section tells you all about it.

Dressing up your salad or bowl

The secret is in the sauce when it comes to vegan salads and bowls. The dressing brings all the components together, unifying them under a common flavor umbrella while complementing their taste. It also prevents your salad from feeling dry.

It's helpful to use common flavor combinations as a base. Get inspired by the spice and flavorings of other favorite dishes and start improvising from there.

Most good dressings include the following ingredient categories:

- Something fatty: Traditionally, oil is used in salad sauces and dressings. The fat molecules transport flavors and enhance the eating experience. Unfortunately, oils are high in calorie and low in vitamins. Don't let that stop you from including a little fat in your dressing! Nut and seed butters, including tahini and hemp butter, add nutrition and amplify flavors all at once. If you have a high-power blender, you can put whole nuts and seeds in the jar and blend until perfectly smooth. Avocado also has some fat that improves dressings — just make sure it's for immediate consumption as the green flesh may partially oxidize and go brown after a day or two depending on your salad's chemistry.

- Something acidic: Acids such as vinegars and citrus juices (lemon, lime, orange) brighten your salad and tone down competing bitterness, which is often present in salads using a base of dark leafy green vegetables. Although some recipes use a small quantity of plain white vinegar, more flavorful options like apple cider vinegar, balsamic vinegar, and plum vinegar will likely add more to your tasting pleasure. Citrus juice helps boost iron absorption, so whenever possible it's a great idea to add some instead of using only vinegar.

- Something salty: Salt increases the flavor of everything… along with our blood pressure. It's an acquired taste that we can wean ourselves off over time by progressively decreasing the amount of salt we add when cooking and at the table. But there is also an interesting substitute: miso. Miso paste is very salty but, according to research discussed by Dr. Michael Greger, the fermentation process involved counteracts the unhealthful effects of the sodium within. Don't go all out on the miso paste, but a teaspoon will go a long way in deepening the flavor of your dressing.

The first few ingredients are the base of the dressing. These additional seasonings will create a unique flavor profile to complement the main components of your dish   :

- Garlic (or garlic powder)
- Ginger (or ginger powder)
- A little onion (or onion powder) or shallot
- Mustard (Dijon, or mustard powder)
- Spices (cumin, chili, turmeric, coriander, paprika, and even a little bit of cinnamon!)
- Herbs (basil, oregano, parsley, thyme, rosemary, cilantro… fresh or dried)
- Pepper
- Nutritional yeast

If there is no fruit in your salad, you may want to add a little sweetness to your dressing. You can blend in a whole date or use a liquid sweetener like molasses or maple syrup. A little goes a long way!

Power blender for the win

If you have a power blender, you can go wild and create a uniquely tasty and nutritious dressing with very little effort.

Not only you can put in the garlic and ginger in big chunks (no need to mince!) or use a whole dried date as a sweetener (remove the pit first), but you can also add whole ingredients like fresh herbs, carrot, or mango, and create a luscious, smooth, and colorful sauce that's bursting with both flavor and nutrients.

Pro-tip: If you don't have a small blender jar, double up the recipe so the blades can really get things spinning. Transfer the extra to a jar, label, and freeze.

Struggling with picky eaters

If some of people at your table are selective eaters, you can still serve them a salad, deconstructed. Make little piles of each of the salad's components on a large plate or cutting board, with the dressing on the side for optional dipping. If some foods are completely new, or on the "no" list, still include them, but in a ridiculously small quantity. Think: 3 grains of couscous, one square-inch sized piece of kale, or a Lilliputian cauliflower floret. You can encourage them to smell, lick, or taste the new foods, but no need to make a big deal of it.

Time saving tactics

The downside of making meal salads and bowls is that they have many different components. They can take a while to prepare if you're working from scratch. Here are a few time-saving tactics:

Big batches of whole grains: Whole grains can take a while to cook, so include a big batch of your favorite in your weekend minimum viable meal prep session. Or just make extra when you cook on a weeknight. Doubling or tripling the amount of grain cooked doesn't take much more time, and it will save you dishwashing time. Just refrigerate in an airtight container. Grains also freeze very well – don't forget to label your containers!

Roast ahead: Roasting vegetables is better done on the weekend, because it takes at least 30 minutes. You can roast two, three, or four baking sheets' worth of veggies to contribute to a few of your weeknights' meals, making the most of your oven's space and energy. If you have an air fryer, you can roast small batches of veggies right before dinner in a reasonable time.

Get your beans where you can: Canned beans are well suited to using in salads. If you want to go extra fancy for a special occasion, it's nice to roast or air-fry the chickpeas or pan-fry them with a smidge of oil for extra crispiness.

No shame in boxed greens: Buying pre-washed greens will save you lots of time. I prefer the "power greens" mix that includes baby kale, Swiss chard, and spinach, or just kale for a more robust nutrition profile. Arugula is also great – and a cruciferous veggie (like kale). The "baby" leaves are more tender and don't require massaging.

Double the dressing: Make twice the amount of dressing or sauce and freeze the extra (with a label!). It will be perfectly fine to use after a good re-shake later.

Pizza

Learning how to make vegan pizza at home is one of the most fun and satisfying cooking activities you can get yourself into... and it's way easier than you think! It's also a great way to get everyone (including kids!) involved in the kitchen.

Above everything, making your own vegan pizza is about finding out that restaurant staples can be even better – in every way – when you make them at home.

Even the worst cook doesn't need to buy ready-made pizza dough

Making your own pizza dough costs pennies, takes mere minutes of hands-on time, and saves you from the plastic packaging that comes with the store-bought type.

Plus, it will give you a dopamine boost from having achieved something awesome all by yourself.

As you craft your own pizza regularly, you may even develop the joy of honing your dough-stretching technique. I'll never get to 10,000 hours of practice in this art myself, but my skills have improved fabulously over the years, along with the texture of my crusts.

Step 1: Proof your yeast

Your kids will love this. If you don't have kids, borrow one from a friend or neighbour.

Add 1 cup of hot water that's about 100 degrees Fahrenheit (40 Celsius) to a big cup. Add 2 teaspoons active dry yeast (or one of those small envelopes) and 1 teaspoon sugar to the water. Stir to dissolve the sugar.

Tip: The water temperature is about the same as a baby bottle (or not-too-hot hot tub). On your wrist, it should feel warmer than your body's temperature, but not so hot that it would burn a precious infant's lips (or bum). If your plumbing and hot water heater are recent, it's probably fine to get the hot water from the tap. Otherwise, use cold tap water and warm it up in a kettle or pot… but don't let it get too hot!

Now tell your kids this: the warm water will gently wake the yeast up, prompting it to eat the sugar for breakfast… and the yeast will fart little bubbles of carbon dioxide.

Give the yeast time to show it's alive and awake, about 5 to 10 minutes.

If after that much time you don't have a nice frothy layer of bubbles, you have a problem. Either you killed the yeast with water that's too hot, or it's drowning in too-cold water, or it was dead to begin with (too old). Fix the problem and start over.

If you make pizza every week, you don't have to repeat the proof test every time. Just keep your jar of yeast in the fridge to ensure freshness. If you are at least 8 hours away from dinnertime, and trust that your yeast isn't too old, then you can skip the proofing test.

Step 2: Mix everything together

This is where things get ugly (in a good way).

In one big metal bowl, combine 3 cups of flour with the

yeast-water-sugar mixture. Add ¼ cup extra water plus ½ teaspoon salt, optionally adding 1 tablespoon of olive oil.

Mix it all up.

If you have a stand mixer with a dough hook, let it do the messy work for a minute or two.

If you don't, do your best with a strong wooden spoon for a minute or two, trying to moisten as much of the flour as possible.

A word on the flour: It's hard to make a nice fluffy pizza with whole wheat flour only. I get the best results with all-purpose flour, and I can integrate whole wheat for up to 1/3 of the total flour weight... but it's not as satisfying. That's why we have pizza once or twice per month, not every day.

Step 3: Wait

You now have many options depending on when you plan on eating the pizza.

If you plan on eating pizza in the next couple of days, but not tonight, just cover the bowl with plastic wrap and put it in the fridge, ugly as it is. Nobody's looking.

If you plan on eating pizza in the next 4 hours, cover the bowl with a wet (but not dripping) towel and stash it in the oven with the light on (but no heat). Or maybe next to a sunny window.

If you plan on eating pizza in the next 4-8 hours, leaving it covered on the countertop is probably good enough unless your home feels cold.

Step 4: Knead a bit

Your dough will have risen to about twice its original volume now.

Dump it out of the bowl and onto the countertop. Knead it into a pretty ball. Use your body weight to avoid straining your wrists. Four or five minutes is plenty.

Or, if you have a stand mixer with a dough hook, pop it in there for another 2 minutes.

Step 5: Wait some more (if you can)

If you have time, you can put the pizza dough back in the lit (but not hot) oven for up to 2 hours, still covered with a moist cloth. The dough will plump up again, giving you the opportunity to deflate it with a satisfying punch before stretching. But this step is not necessary, just desirable.

Advanced prepper tip: Double up on all ingredients, and when you reach this stage split the dough in half. Wrap the half you don't need tightly, using plastic wrap and a zip-top bag. Freeze for up to 6 months. You can freeze in smaller portions, so it thaws faster, too.

Step 6: Stretch

Now is the time to fire up the oven – just make sure it's empty first because it's about to get really hot!

Go as hot as it will, around 450 to 500 degrees Fahrenheit (240 Celsius, gas mark 9). High temperature will improve your crust.

If you have a pizza stone, put it in the oven to heat it up for 20 minutes or more.

Sprinkle your work surface with a flour and keep about ¼ cup extra in case you need it.

Divide your dough into two pieces (or more if making mini pizzas) and use your hands, assisted by gravity, to stretch into something like a circle. Oval and rectangular pizza is great, too.

Work by hand as much as you can, but don't beat yourself up if you need to pull out a rolling pin.

Put in a good effort but do not expect perfection. Practice will make progress, which is a good reason to make pizza at home at least once per month.

Step 7: Cover up!

If you are using a pizza stone, but don't have a pizza peel, I recommend transferring your stretched dough onto a sheet of parchment paper that will fit your stone nicely.

If using a baking sheet or pan (round or not, doesn't matter!), I recommend oiling it first by spreading a teaspoon of oil or two on the bottom, using your fingers or a brush. It will make removal easier. Alternatively, a generous sprinkle of cornmeal will help with removal. Or just use parchment paper as a liner.

Don't let technicalities stop you. My pizza isn't completely round, and my pan isn't made for a pie, but I still enjoy delicious pizza.

Step 8: Garnish

Start with a layer of tomato sauce, pesto, hummus, nutty sauce, or anything saucy, really.

Then add your favorite toppings. Here are some ideas:

- Chunky walnut pesto, thinly sliced potatoes (softened in salted water for 30 minutes), and a sprinkle of chili peppers (add slices of vegan sausage for hungry t-rexes)
- Roasted cauliflower, carrots, and chickpeas with tomato sauce and a drizzle of cashew cream
- Roasted mushrooms and red peppers with a sprinkle of corn kernels and baby arugula thrown on top as soon as it comes out of the oven (the arugula will wilt immediately)

- Artichoke hearts over a layer of kalamata olive tapenade, sprinkled with lots of vegan feta
- Nacho pizza: black beans and onions sautéed together with a bit of adobo pepper then puréed, dropped onto a base of tomato sauce, and sprinkled with diced onions and green olives, with a drizzle of cheesy sauce or vegan jack-style shreds – sprinkle with sliced green onions when it comes out of the oven
- Good ol' vegan pepperoni and cheeze (my kids' favorite)

Step 9: Bake

Time to pop that pizza in the oven! Different toppings will need different timing, but generally you should start keeping a close eye on it after 10 minutes. It should certainly not take more than 20 minutes for the crust to be kissed with golden brown spots.

Carefully remove the pizza from the oven and let it rest for 2-3 minutes before slicing.

Dinner leftovers as vegan pizza toppings

Once you know the trick, making pizza dough is so easy, you'll want excuses to make pizza more often.

Friday night, when you survey the fridge for leftovers, make note of what would work well as a pizza topping. Be creative! Any cooked vegetable, legume, or vegan meat can be combined with a few flavor bombs (olives, spicy sauces, kimchi, chutney, etc.) to garnish your pie.

Before going to bed, mix the dough ingredients and pop them in the fridge.

Come Saturday night, you get to relax as you stretch your dough into shape, perhaps with a fancy beverage.

Put pizza into your weekly vegan meal prep

Pizza doesn't have to be the stuff of special occasions! If you batch cook on Sunday, take 5 minutes to mix your dough and let it ferment in the fridge for 2-3 days. On the night when you want to eat pizza, quickly stretch and garnish it while the oven preheats. It will feel like a treat! Yet it's so simple.

INSTANT SAUCES

There are days when everything seems to go wrong. By the time dinner time rolls around, my energy bucket is just empty. It's tempting to take a break from cooking, but the truth is: a home-made platter of pasta will be far more comforting than anything I can get ready-made.

When that happens, I like to whip up an instant sauce following one of the three recipes below. Although the exact recipe changes from one time to the next, the results are always the same: a healthy and tasty quick vegan pasta dish. Yum!

In this section, I will teach you how to (almost) instantly make sauce for your pasta, using pantry ingredients and leftover produce. Next time you're craving a fast and comforting dinner, you'll be able to create a delish and quick vegan pasta dish… lickety split.

Optional starting step: roast some vegetables

When you walk into the kitchen, preheat the oven to 375 degrees Fahrenheit (190 Celsius, gas mark 5) right away, just in case you find something in the produce drawer that will go well with your pasta. And I bet you will! The following veggies make amazing pasta companions:

- mushrooms (quartered or sliced thickly)
- cabbage of any color (chopped into chunks)
- red or sweet onions (chopped into chunks)

- carrots (sliced into half-moons, not too thick, not too thin)
- red or orange bell peppers (big slices)
- cauliflower (just hack it into chunks, no time to preciously separate the florets)

Toss your findings with salt and pepper, perhaps adding 2 teaspoons of olive oil. That's optional. Line a baking sheet with parchment paper (to make clean up quicker) and spread your veggies on it in a single layer. Don't crowd them too much or they'll steam instead of roast! Slide that into the oven. They'll be ready in 30, or whenever the pasta and sauce are done. You can toss them a bit at the halfway point, but really if you forget it's not a big deal.

First required step: set a pot of water to boil

Fill your big pasta pot to halfway mark or a little more, put it on your biggest element, and turn it up on high. Now turn your attention to what you can do for a sauce. But keep an eye on it: as soon as it boils, you can throw in the pasta.

Idea #1: Creamy hummus

It doesn't get easier than that. It would be embarrassing to call it a recipe! All you need for this instant vegan sauce is to have at hand is about 1 cup of hummus, whether it's store-bought or home-made.

1. Bring a big pot of water to a boil, add your pasta of choice, and cook for the suggested amount of time.
2. Just before draining, cautiously use a ladle or a measuring cup with a handle to scoop out 1 cup of the pasta's cooking water.
3. Quickly drain the pasta then return it to the hot pot. Do not return the pot to the heat. Throw in a big scoop of

hummus – between 2/3 cup and 1 ½ cups depending on your taste (and the amount of pasta) – and stir quickly to coat. Add in some of the pasta cooking water to make the hummus "sauce" creamier. Start with ¼ cup cooking water and add more if needed.

4. There is no step 4! Unless you happen to have baby greens like young arugula, spinach, kale, or chard at hand, in which case you can throw in a handful into the pot right now and stir again.

Variations

In the unlikely event that there isn't hummus already in your fridge, you can make something similar by throwing in the blender some cooked chickpeas (or white beans), lemon juice, tahini (or a small handful of nuts), and garlic, plus a bit of the pasta's cooking water.

You could also use any other kind of vegan spread you have at hand, like a cashew "cream cheese," and follow the same procedure.

Idea #2: Pesto-ish

This instant sauce idea requires a blender or food processor, but even a not-so-great one will do – as long as you don't mind a chunky pesto.

1. Bring a big pot of water to a boil.
2. While the pasta water is heating up, add some or all the following ingredients to your blender:
   - handfuls of young greens (baby arugula, spinach, kale… even carrot tops!) and/or herbs (parsley, cilantro, basil…) (up to 3-4 cups)

- handful of nuts or seeds (¼ to ¾ cup) like walnuts, almonds, pumpkin seeds, sunflower seeds, hemp seeds, pine nuts, cashews, macadamia nuts… go for a mix of a few of those if you'd like, but don't add more than about ¾ cup
- lemon juice (2-6 tablespoons) or even half of a peeled lemon (make sure there are no seeds)
- garlic (fresh or garlic powder), a few cloves or 1 teaspoon of garlic powder
- nutritional yeast, 2-4 tablespoons

3. Pulse a few times to start integrating the ingredients.

4. When the pasta water boils, cook your pasta for the suggested amount of time (see package). Just before draining, using a measuring cup with a handle or a ladle, remove about 2 cups of cooking water from the pot and set aside.

5. Drain the pasta and return to the hot pot. Do not return to the burner.

6. Add 1 cup of the pasta cooking water to your blender, make sure the lid is on tight, and process for a few seconds to a minute, depending on the desired texture. Add water, two tablespoons at a time, as needed.

7. Quickly transfer the blended pesto sauce from your blender to the pasta in the hot pot and stir to coat. Cover the pot.

8. If desired, you can add a little more of the cooking water to your blender and process to "clean" the sides. Add to the pasta if you like saucy things.

Variations

Instead of young greens, you can use any cooked vegetable you have. Leftover roasted cauliflower, yam, beets, and squash, among others, make luscious sauces.
Carrots are a popular ingredient for a cheesy sauce.

If you don't have cooked veggies, you can quickly chop a couple of cups of raw vegetables and cook them in the boiling water, before cooking the pasta. Either steam them in a basket over your boiling water or throw them straight in and scoop them out with a slotted spoon after about 8 minutes. Follow the rest of the steps as described above and you'll soon have a brightly colored sauce to highlight your pasta.

Idea #3: Nutty Alfredo

To make a Nutty Alfredo sauce that rivals the decadence of its dairy counterparts, without advance soaking of the nuts, a high-power blender is essential. Because I love this vegan Alfredo sauce so much, it would on its own be worth the price of the Vitamix to me.

1. Bring a big pot of water to boil.
2. While the pasta water is heating up, add some or all the following ingredients to your blender:
   - handful of raw nuts or seeds (½ to 1 cup) like walnuts, almonds, pumpkin seeds, sunflower seeds, hemp seeds, pine nuts, cashews, macadamia nuts… go for a mix of a few of those if you'd like, but don't add more than about 1 cup. Keep in mind that pumpkin and hemp seeds will give your sauce a green tinge.
   - garlic (fresh or garlic powder), a few cloves or 1 teaspoon of garlic powder

- onion powder, about 1 teaspoon
- miso paste (about 2 teaspoons) or some salt
- fresh ground black pepper
- perhaps ½ teaspoon paprika
- optional nutritional yeast, 1 to 2 tablespoons

3. When the water boils, cook pasta for the suggested amount of time (see package). Just before draining, using a measuring cup with a handle or a ladle, remove about 2 cups of cooking water from the pot and set aside.

4. Drain the pasta and return to the hot pot, but off the heat.

5. Add 1 cup of the pasta cooking water to your blender, make sure the lid is on tight, and process for 30 seconds to a minute. Add water, two tablespoons at a time, as needed.

6. Quickly transfer the creamy sauce from your blender to the pasta in the hot pot and stir to coat. Cover the pot.

7. If desired, you can add a little more of the cooking water to your blender and process to "clean" the sides. Add to the pasta if you like saucy things.

8. I love to enjoy this vegan Alfredo pasta with a few handfuls of baby arugula tossed in. I just throw it in at the same time as the sauce and it wilts in a flash. Any leftover baby greens (kale, spinach, mizuna…) will be fantastic here.

9. Top it up with the roasted veggies (if you have them).

I like to use tongs to twist the pasta into a nest and serve into shallow bowls, with the roasted vegetables on top.

For a nice finishing touch, add a sprinkling of nuts and/or nutritional yeast, or a few sprigs of fresh herbs. Or just wolf it down without further ado!

Make it more filling

To me, a quick vegan pasta dish like this is pretty filling. But if you must feed a hungry T-rex, construction worker, or growing teenager, you may want to consider adding thick slices of store-bought vegan sausage to your roasting pan along with the veggies. A whole-food option is to drain a can of chickpeas, quickly pat the peas dry, and toss with 2 teaspoons of olive oil, salt, and pepper. Roast on a baking sheet at the same time as the veggies and sprinkle on top of the dish.

VEGETABLES TO BUY EVERY WEEK

There are ten vegetables that show up every week on my grocery list. We eat them most days of the week. They are on my meal plans, and at the base of practically every meal I improvise. Most of them are robust enough to keep well in the refrigerator for two or more weeks, which means that I can stock enough in the produce drawer to know I can cook up any meal without a recipe. Combined with a few of my other vegan pantry staples (see next section), they form the base of our meals, and of our good health.

Red onions

Practically everything I cook in a week starts with chopping a red onion. They are inexpensive nutritional powerhouses that fight cancer and many other diseases, and they deepen the flavor of every savory dish one can imagine. I prefer red onions because they are sweet and have more phytonutrients, as the bright-colored skin and layers demonstrate.

I always keep at least 3-5 red onions in the fridge. In the winter here in Vancouver, as long as temperatures don't dip below freezing level, I keep a big bag of onions in a box on our deck. (If you live somewhere colder, keep them in the garage so they don't freeze.) Chopping onions when they are cold, as opposed to room temperature, prevents uncontrollable crying.

Save time (and your fingers): Proper chopping technique will save you hours every month. Make sure to review my blog post on basic knife skills.[6]

Garlic

Garlic is another vegetable that I always, always, always keep at hand. I wouldn't want to make soup, stews, stir-fries, risottos, or, well, anything, without it. Not only garlic helps prevent the common cold and cancer, but it adds depth and flavor to my meals. If a recipe calls for one clove, I use two or three.

I prefer purple garlic because the large, even-sized cloves are faster to split and mince, and the flavor is milder when served raw. As much as possible, I buy it from a local source and avoid the imported white garlic. Big cheap bags of peeled garlic cloves are easy to find these days but unfortunately (in my experience) they don't taste like much. Don't let the price or convenience sway you: it's not worth it.

Common advice says to store garlic on the countertop in a special clay pot, but I just put mine in the refrigerator's butter compartment (which conveniently contains no butter).

Heath-boosting tip: Dr. Michael Greger of nutritionfacts.org recommends using the "chop and stop" method to maximize the health benefits of garlic. I just chop the garlic first and let it sit on the side while I chop the onions, so it has maximized its allicin production by the time I throw it in the hot skillet.

Ginger

Ginger shows up in three to five of my dinners every week.

---

6   Basic knife skills: https://veganfamilykitchen.com/how-to-cook-everything-faster-learn-basic-knife-skills/

More associated with Asian and Middle Eastern dishes, it's usually included in stir-fries, curry, couscous, fried rice, and sauces, such as my personal favorite Friday-night dinner: Coco-peanut noodles. It adds a warming zing that awakens taste buds. In addition, regular ginger consumption reduces muscle soreness - good news for a runner like me!

Stop wasting your time peeling ginger! The skin is fine to eat. Just scrub the ginger root like a potato and use the finest side of a box grater (or a microplane) to mince it. No-one will be able to tell the difference. If the root is shriveled, chop off the sad parts before mincing.

I find organic ginger offers smaller roots but a more potent flavor, so it requires less.

Carrots

Yummy carrots are worth paying a few extra bucks for if you can find a consistent source. There is no clear indication that organic carrots are more nutritious than their conventional counterparts. But somehow, in my experience, they look better and taste sweeter. In season, I prefer local above all because that's how I get the freshest tops to make pesto.

Cooking increases the health benefits of carrots. Their beta-carotenoids get converted into vitamin A by our bodies, benefiting eye health.

Carrots are another vegetable I rarely peel. A vigorous brush takes care of residual specks of dirt. Just chop to add to any simmered dish. On their own, they make a beautiful soup, too. Roasted, they are perfectly sweet.

Just because they are better-for-us cooked doesn't mean I never eat them raw. They are a convenient and crunchy way to carry hummus and other bean dips to my mouth. I also love grating them to add a pop of orange to big lunch salads. Combine them with red cabbage, a diced apple, and some pumpkin seeds.

Orange sweet potatoes (which you may think of as yam)

Let's clarify something right away: aren't yam and sweet potatoes the same thing? No! Let me quote what the sweet potato expert, Jenné Clairborne, says about the difference between sweet potatoes and yams:

> "Sweet potatoes belong to the morning glory family and are usually orange and sweet with moist, starchy flesh. They are distantly related to potatoes, but they are not nightshades. Sweet potatoes and yams are not at all related. Yams are native to Africa and Asia and have starchy white flesh and gray-brown skin. They aren't nearly as nutritious as sweet potatoes and have much lower yield." (Jenné Clairborne, on p. 29 of her *Sweet Potato Soul* book, which is fantastic by the way.)

Jenné further describes nine varieties of sweet potatoes that can be found in North American grocery stores, and they all sound amazing.

Don't peel them! A vigorous brushing will do. The skin has 10 times the phytonutrients as the flesh, which is almost as much as blueberries.

I have two favorite uses for sweet potatoes. The first is to make them into a peanutty stew with chickpeas. The second is simply to halve and roast them (let's say 40 minutes at 375 degrees Fahrenheit or 190 Celsius) and top with a simple black bean stew (onion, garlic, black beans, with cumin, oregano, and a bit of chipotle pepper for seasoning), with a drizzle of cashew cream. So good! They are a great item to roast as part of a "minimum viable prep" on the weekend and serve with bowls.

Alternative use: Do like Dr. Greger and cook two sweet potatoes in the microwave before leaving the house on a cold day. Wrap in foil (after microwaving!) and pop them in your pockets to serve as handwarmers on your way to work. Enjoy them as a snack later!

Cauliflower, broccoli, and other cruciferous vegetables

There always are cruciferous veggies on my grocery list. Not only they are a category of their own on Dr. Greger's Daily Dozen, for their many health benefits, but they provide a broad diversity of flavors from bitter to sweet, along with a dose of crunch. Colorful, too!

A handful of broccoli florets can be thrown into the pasta's boiling water to make a simple, tasty, and nutritious pasta dish. Cauliflower can always be roasted with a sprinkle of spices for a satisfying addition to salads, although I am always surprised at how sweet it is raw, too.

Time-saving tip: Cauliflower can be a little harder to cut into florets than broccoli... so often I don't! If I'm in the slightest rush, I just chop the whole head of cauliflower, stem included, into thumb-sized pieces. It's just fine for soups and stews of all kinds. The only time I worry about creating individual florets is if I am assembling a crudité platter.

Kale

Another cruciferous veggie that's worth buying every single week! Kale is an essential ingredient of my smoothies but also shows up in simmered dishes, tofu scrambles, bowls, and salads. The bigger the pieces, the more you should massage them to break down their tough fibers. One quick way to do it is to wash the leaves under running water, rip the tender parts off the stem, and pile them on top of a clean tea towel. Roll and wring the towel as hard as you can. It's great exercise for your hands and gets the job done quickly and cleanly.

Less food waste, more nutrition: Why throw away the tough stems? Just slice them thinly and add at the same time as the onion when starting any cooked dish. They have all the same nutrients as the leaves, and extra fiber. It's one of my favorite natural nutrition boosters.

What variety? I prefer Lacinato kale (also called "black" or "dinosaur") for a very practical reason: the leaves are flatter and fit better in my fridge. The best strategy is to vary which kind you buy (and eat!) every week, to enjoy a full range of different nutrients and gustatory experiences.

If you are just getting started, buy a single bunch (usually 5 to 7 leaves) and aim to eat at least one leaf per person per day.

Mushrooms

Technically, mushrooms are not vegetables but part of a different kingdom (fungus as opposed to plants). But do not let technicalities stop you from consuming them every day on a plant-based diet!

Mushrooms contain even more water per weight than most vegetables. They pack many nutrients with health benefits. Plus, they provide a nice variety in texture and mouthfeel that can either enhance vegan dishes *or* stand on their own as the main act, like grilled portobello caps.

Allowed to breathe in a paper bag, mushrooms will keep for a solid week and perhaps a little longer in your fridge. I always have them on hand to add to stir-fries and Asian-style noodle soups, or to sauté for a quick topping on risotto or pasta sauce. Friday night dinner at my home almost always contain them as the "last veggies standing" from the produce drawer, along with some cabbage, in a nutty blender sauce.

Cabbage

Why isn't everyone eating cabbage all the time? It's so good! And so cheap. I wish I had a second fridge to always stock at least two heads: one red and one green. I find red cabbage to be a better fit to add color, crunch, and nutrition to bowls and salads (even better when combined with grated carrots, see above). The green type turns decadently sweet (while being nothing but healthy) when grilled in thick slices with a pinch of salt. Because I am short on fridge space, I usually go for a not-too-big head of red cabbage that we chop at through the week.

Pre-washed power greens

This is a hard one for me to admit, because I try hard to reduce the amount of plastic packaging we use. But here's the hard truth: when I don't have the opportunity to visit the farmers' market to buy baby greens in bulk, I often turn to boxed or bagged pre-washed power greens from the supermarket. I look for those with kale, chard, and spinach, or other more-robust greens, as opposed to "mixed greens" or "salad greens" which contain more lettuce.

Whatever you are cooking, just add a handful. It'll wilt right in! If you'd rather have multiple dishes on the table, put a giant handful in a side bowl for a salad, add some grated carrot and shredded red cabbage, plus a few bonus salad ingredients from your vegan pantry staples, such as raisins and hemp seeds.

Have them for breakfast, too! Combine with juicy fruit (apple, orange, and pineapple come to mind) and a pitted date or two. Add plant milk (or, if you have a powerful blender, a handful of nuts or seeds with a cup of water). Blend until smooth and voilà! Bright green smoothie.

Unlike the other veggies from my vegan grocery list above, mixed greens have a much shorter lifespan in the fridge. Even if you live alone, you should make it through a small or medium box in four days. If there's any left over after that, just add extra to your smoothie.

MUST-HAVE PANTRY INGREDIENTS

What if you could improvise practically any dinner, using just pantry ingredients and some fresh produce? It's possible with a well-stocked selection of vegan pantry staples.

I compiled the list of the most frequently used ingredients that go into my family's dinners at home. Since I practically always cook from the same Vegan Meal Plans my clients use, I created a big spreadsheet with one year's worth of meal plans ingredients based on the shopping lists. I then counted the number of times each ingredient appeared. The list below contains those vegan pantry staples I use every week, plus a few that I use only occasionally – but at least once per season.

These pantry staples are all either non-perishable, or stable for a long time when refrigerated. If you stock most of the vegan pantry staples from this list, you will not only be able to cook practically all meals from the Vegan Family Meal Plans, but also improvise dinner when you need to.

On occasion, you may hit a recipe for which you are missing an ingredient or two. In 99% of cases, the missing ingredient can be replaced with one of those you already have in your vegan pantry. If you need suggestions for substitutions, feel free to reach out to me using the chat box on my website.

All these vegan pantry staples are plant-based – except mushrooms (which are fungi) and salt (which is a mineral). For the most part, those ingredients are also whole, or minimally transformed.

Whenever possible and reasonable, purchase those ingredients in bulk and store them in clear glass containers with airtight lids. This will protect your food inventory against pantry moths, avoid food waste, and speed up cooking.

Vegan pantry staples can be divided among just a few categories: legumes, grains and pseudo-grains and their products, nuts and seeds, spices and flavorings, and canned goods, in addition to a small number of miscellaneous shelf-stable and refrigerated items.

All the beans: pillars of plant-based eating

The following pulses show up on our table every month, and in some cases every week:

- Chickpeas: our everyday favorite.
- Black beans: a very close second.
- White/cannellini beans: perfect on its own, but also great to add nourishment and thickness to soups. They can even be blended into the batter of baked items, pancakes, or waffles.
- Red lentils: add a handful to every soup or stew you make, no-one will notice.
- Green or brown lentils: excellent as a base for vegan burgers and meatballs.
- French "de Puy" lentils: firmer and more suitable for bowls and salads.
- Yellow split peas: perfect for soups and stews.

- Black-eyed peas: when you can't decide between a black bean and a cannellini...

I prefer cooking my beans from dry, but canned beans are perfectly acceptable too. (If you can find BPA-free cans, even better.) Every Friday, immediately after reviewing the coming week's meal plan, I pull the dry beans I'll need from the pantry and soak the required quantities, plus more for lunches and snacks. Saturday morning, I drain the soaked beans and cook them in my Instant Pot.

There are some beans I use only occasionally, like kidney, lima, and pinto. I tend to buy them canned if they make an appearance on the meal plan (or substitute for a dry bean I have on hand).

Grains and pseudo-grains: carbs are good for us

The grain-free diet fad is one I just can't get behind or even understand. Carbohydrates are humans' primary source of energy and grains are a great source of carbs. Within this general category, it is wise to choose ingredients that also bring other nutritional value, such as a wealth of fiber and vitamins that nurture a healthy heart and digestive system. Here are my favorites:

- Red and brown rice (review cooking method in the section about Cooking whole grains)
- Quinoa
- Farro
- Wheatberries
- Barley (pot barley is closer to whole but pearl cooks faster)
- Oats: from whole groats to quick-cook, your choice

Millet isn't featured on this list because I haven't eaten much of it in the past, but I'm working on adding more of it to our meals as a substitute for rice. Like quinoa and farro, it makes a great building block for bowls.

Some convenient, lightly processed grain products

Although I agree in theory that it is preferable to populate our meal plans with whole grains, as opposed to flour-based products, I still need the convenience of some lightly processed grain products to enable my cooking goals. If you are trying to reduce your weight for health reasons, I recommend engaging with the material in Dr. Michael Greger's *How Not to Diet* book and de-flouring your diet. If you are at a healthy weight, enjoying these shortcuts a few times per week seems like a reasonable practice if you also consume a lot of whole grains and vegetables.

- Pasta: I always stock some long, quick-cooking ones (spaghettini) and a couple of varieties of short ones. If you are just getting acquainted with whole wheat pasta, start with quick-cook varieties like spaghettini before moving your way to thicker shapes like penne.
- Asian noodles: buckwheat (soba) and rice noodles are our favorites but when I visit a Korean grocer, I love buying some bean- and yam-based noodles too. I use all of those interchangeably.
- Couscous (preferably whole wheat): cooks in 5 minutes all included, can't be beat for speed!
- Gnocchi: these pillow-like potato dumplings make weeknight dinner feel like a special occasion.
- Arborio rice: makes the creamiest risottos!

- Whole wheat and all-purpose flour: I combine these two to make pizza (1/3 whole wheat, 2/3 all purpose) once a month.

Nuts, seeds, and dried fruit

Every meal can benefit from a sprinkle of nuts and seeds. They impart a contrast in texture and color, in addition to their many nutrients. Dried fruit add sweetness and iron to bowls and even to some stews without having to chop anything.

- Almonds
- Walnuts
- Cashews
- Sesame seeds (and tahini, which is sesame seed butter)
- Sunflower seeds
- Hemp seeds
- Pumpkin seeds
- Flax seeds (whole, plus a small, separate jar with a week's worth of ground flax seeds to make it easy to sprinkle it everywhere)
- Raisins, currants, and cranberries
- Dates (added to blended sauces instead of a sweetener)

Whenever a dish calls for nut or seed butter, I just throw the whole version in the blender. If you do not have a high-power blender, you may want to stock almond butter and maybe pumpkin butter.

The ingredients above are those I use for dinner. To cover for snacks and breakfasts (and in particular my favorite morning meal: overnight oats), I would add the following:

- peanuts
- hemp seeds
- chia seeds

- prunes
- Goji berries
- Brazil nuts (just to have Dr. Greger's 4 per month)

Spices for life

My favorite dishes are inspired by Mexican, Indian, and Asian cuisines. Whenever possible, I prefer to buy whole spices then grind and combine them myself, rather than buying ready-made mixes, because it decreases my odds of consuming adulterated spices spiked with fillers. (Unfortunately, fraud is extremely common in the spice industry.) Here are my favorites, from those I use most often to those I use less frequently:

- Peppercorns
- Salt
- Cumin (I keep them both whole and ground)
- Turmeric (ground)
- Oregano
- Thyme
- Garlic powder
- Red chili flakes and chili powder
- Coriander (whole and ground)
- Smoked paprika
- Cinnamon
- Mustard powder (add a pinch when cooking cruciferous veggies for maximum cancer-fighting power)
- Onion powder
- Rosemary
- Black salt (also known as kala namak, to add that "eggy" taste to tofu for scrambles)
- Bay leaves

Other flavorings that make a world of difference

If you think vegan food is bland, you need to up your flavoring game! In addition to the spices above, I use the following seasonings on a regular basis.

- Vegetable broth powder: I use a lot of broth, but I don't have the space to make big batches of my own, nor the carrying capacity to bring containers of prepared broth back home. Instead, I use a quality powdered vegetable broth, and dissolve it in boiling water. In addition to my everyday option (made by GoBio), I love using Better Than Bouillon beef-less and chicken-less pastes for special dishes.
- Balsamic vinegar
- Nutritional yeast flakes: for that cheesy taste
- Soy sauce (low-sodium) and/or tamari
- Apple cider vinegar
- Vegan Worcestershire sauce (the non-vegan option has anchovies)
- Various hot sauces: my husband adds some to almost everything.
- Rice vinegar
- Truffle oil (a few drops suffice!)
- Liquid smoke
- Dried mushrooms

Canned goods: useful shortcuts

These simple ingredients are a must to create for a wide range of dishes, including instant sauces (see section on instant sauces):

- Tomatoes in 28-ounce cans (crushed or diced)
- Tomato paste

- Tomato sauce for pizza
- Jackfruit in water or brine (not in syrup)
- Coconut milk: a once-in-a-while indulgence
- Roasted red peppers
- Sundried tomatoes
- Kalamata olives

Many people will add "pasta sauce" to the list here but I prefer making my own with onion, garlic, and canned tomatoes.

Miscellaneous pantry ingredients

Some ingredients just have a hard time fitting into categories:

- Kombu: added to the cooking water of beans to cover our iodine needs, since we don't always use iodized salt. (See section on Cooking dry beans from scratch.)
- Wakame: for miso soup and snacking.
- Arrowroot powder: as a thickener instead of cornstarch (just to avoid corn products, but really, it's not a big deal).

Refrigerated ingredients

These ingredients are always in my fridge:

- Lemon and lime juices: I found a brand that tastes like the real thing, enabling me to use it more often. (The vitamin C from citrus boosts iron absorption.)
- Miso paste: adds umami and saltiness to sauces (without the downsides of plain salt) and is essential to make miso soup.
- Tofu (firm and extra-firm): we love it for its versatility. If there is tofu in the fridge, there can be dinner on the table. (Technically, it is not stable for more than a few weeks in the refrigerator, but we eat it faster than that!)
- Basic condiments like ketchup, Dijon mustard, and vegan mayo: we use very small amounts of those,

perhaps one jar of each per year for our family of four, but they are good to have on hand and never go bad.

- Kimchi (check that it has no anchovies or shrimp): a forkful enlivens any Asian dish.
- Active dry yeast: for monthly pizza night.
- Baking powder: used quite rarely for dinners but keeps for a very long time in the fridge.
- Maple syrup: I'm from Québec and sometimes can't resist adding a teaspoon to a tomato dish that turned out too acidic.

Frozen ingredients

Whenever possible, I pick fresh produce. But if using frozen veggies saves us from ordering take-out, I go for it without hesitation.

- Edamame (with and without shells): for snacking, bowls, and even pesto!
- Green peas
- Corn kernels
- Mixed veggies
- Potato wedges (for oven fries)

What about oils?

Our family is healthy with no warning signs of heart disease or chronic concerns, and we do not struggle with weight. I don't feel bad using a very small quantity of oil, usually a teaspoon or two when roasting vegetables or sautéing tofu. But oils are by no means necessary vegan pantry staples so I won't list them here.

Make the most of your pantry investments

I have seen vegan shopping lists with over 300 ingredients, but my kitchen and stomach are only so big. I prefer to keep my pantry streamlined, which also helps me reduce food waste. Even long-lasting ingredients are not eternal. You should plan on having at least a once-a-year vegan pantry challenge to review and refresh your stocks.[7]

Keep on Learning

The following resources are trustworthy when it comes to learning about healthy vegan food and cooking.

- **Dr. Michael Greger and his crew at NutritionFacts. org**: Dr. Greger is the biggest nutrition nerd. Along with dozens of volunteers, he closely monitors the peer-reviewed nutrition literature. They distill their findings and put them in context in hundreds of videos in lay language. Dr. Greger's 2015 book *How Not to Die* is a masterpiece that brings it all together in one thoroughly referenced summary that carefully balances views of individual trees with a bird's eye view of the forest. A must-read!

- **The Plant-Based Briefing Podcast** is a curated content podcast where host Marian Erikson shares, with permission, information from various reputable sources about plant-based and vegan topics in ten-minute episodes every day. I always learn something new!

- **Dr. Shireen Kassam** is a UK hematologist and lifestyle medicine physician. I recommend her book *Eating Plant-Based: Scientific Answers to Your Nutrition Questions* as well as her weekly summary of new scientific publications related to plant-based nutrition, available at shireenkassam.medium.com.

- **Pamela Fergusson** is a Canadian registered dietitian. Her no-nonsense Instagram feed @drpamela.rd is useful and inspiring. Her book *Going Vegan for Beginners* is a great introduction to nutrition for plant-based people.
- **Drs. Dean and Ayesha Sherzai** are neurologists dedicated to promoting lifestyle medicine for the prevention and management of Alzheimer's disease. Their book *The Alzheimer's Solution* is powerful, and they share many resources on their web site, TheBrainDocs.com.
- The book *Mind if I Order the Cheeseburger* by Cornell Law professor **Sherry F. Colb** is a treasure trove for anyone who values a good argument. She tackles the questions that vegans are frequently asked with humor, facts, and rational discourse.
- Buddhist monk **Thich Nhat Hanh**'s work, including his tiny book *How to Eat*, inspired me to think differently about cooking.

ACKNOWLEDGMENTS

My clients, newsletter subscribers, and everyone who reads my posts and attends my workshops inspired this book. I am grateful to have a loyal audience of people who want to eat more plants. You know who you are! Your dedication to cooking really good food for yourself and your loved ones inspires and challenges me to continue developing useful resources. I love learning from you.

My friends and online mates Louisa B., Alberto E., Katherina J., Joseph S., Mike W., Pamela S., April B., Gavin F., Jule W., Gary D., Daniel W., and Lori W. have been a source of inspiration and support throughout. Every person I have worked with on Focusmate over the past two years also deserves some credit for helping me make this book happen! We got this.

I am eternally indebted to Élise Desaulniers, whose books got me started on this vegan journey. Thanks to George Kao for the guidance and encouragement, as well as for regularly asking me "How's the book coming along?" I am also grateful that you let me share your "energy reboot" practice with my readers.

The following people read versions of this book's manuscript and I am thankful for their thoughtful comments: Ann Paluska, Caryn Ginsberg, Erin Thompson, Gaye Paterson, Sue Davis, Gemma McFall, Marian Erikson, Shannon Jennings, and Tracey Pordon.

I am above all grateful for the amazing people who share my table every night: my kind and fun children Chloe and Eric, and my loving and open-minded husband Chris, who also carefully read every page. You have been nothing but supportive since I started my plant-based and vegan journey back in 2013. I feel especially lucky that you decided to hop into this lifestyle with me, as it gives even more meaning to our partnership. Special thanks go to my mother-in-law Nona for her amazing plant-based curries and bowls, and father-in-law Bob for his support.

I was raised on real food cooked — and often grown — at home. My mother, Michelle, made every meal from scratch and ensured we always had a choice of homemade desserts. My father, Bertrand, would walk into to the field behind our house in the dark when we wanted a few ears of corn as a bedtime snack. Without their nurturing, I wouldn't have developed this passion for really good food. Thank you. Dad, I wish you were still here to read my book and argue with me on the finer points.

Any remaining mistakes or errors in the book are entirely my responsibility. Please point them out to me so they can be corrected by emailing hello@veganfamilykitchen.com.

I am blessed to live on the traditional unceded territory of the xʷməθkʷəy̓əm (Musqueam), Sḵwx̱wú7mesh (Squamish), and səlilwətaɬ (Tsleil-Waututh) Nations.

Download your Flow in the Kitchen Kit

Visit my website to download your free kit of *Flow in the Kitchen* resources to start and continue your practice.

http://veganfamilykitchen.com/flow-readers/

Keep on cooking!

Please Leave a Review

Did you find the book helpful in your healthy vegan cooking journey? Please share your thoughts with others! Reviews are critical to help books reach the people who need them. Even short, simple ones make a big difference.

Amazon and Goodreads are two good places to leave a review.

You can also write to me at hello@veganfamilykitchen.com.

I am most grateful for your feedback and for helping me support more people who want to eat more plants.

Brigitte Gemme

Printed in Great Britain
by Amazon

26443465R00121